MW00634987

Disclaimer and Warning

CP Technologies believes it has exercised due diligence in the completeness of the instructions in this book. The use of this book is beyond the control of CP Technologies. Consequently, CP Technologies disclaims any liability for it's use. Such disclaimer includes, but is not limited to property damage and personal injury to the Buyer and to others, both public and private and to mishaps deriving from the mixing, casting, storage, usage, transportation of propellant and production of rocket motors and rockets described in this book or designed from this book. The Buyer of this book agrees that in purchasing this book and/or using rocket motors and/or rockets designed from this book that he/she is responsible for all public or private liabilities arising from their use. The Buyer certifies that he/she has read and understands CP Technologies instructions and disclaimer for this book and to use and operate rocket motors and rockets from this book in a safe manner. The Buyer agrees to use the rocket motors and rockets in this book in a safe location and in a manner that does not present a danger to starting residential, property, building, range, grass or forest fires and is solely responsible and liable for any such fires. The Buyer acknowledges that failure of his or her airframe could result in propellant, delay or black powder ejection charge burning at or near ground level.

The procedures in this book involve the handling of ammonium nitrate, ammonium perchlorate, magnesium powder, aluminum powder, black powder and other dangerous chemicals. They must be treated with the greatest of care and respect at all times. The mixing and casting of propellant and handling of black powder should not be attempted by anyone under the age of 18 unless supervised by an adult.

Never store rocket motors near any potential ignition source such as wall heaters, water heaters, stoves, fireplaces, hot appliances or any source of flame.

Always wear safety glasses when mixing and casting propellant.

Never smoke when mixing, casting or handling propellant. Never smoke when handling metal powders, black powder or rocket motors.

"How to Make Amateur Rockets - 2nd Edition"
7th Printing

Distribution by:

CP Technologies
3745 Studer, Unit A
Casper, WY 82604

Web Site: www.space-rockets.com

ISBN: 978-0-9841800-2-8

Acknowledgments

I would like to give a very big thank you to Gary Dwyer for all his assistance and advice in putting the original book together. He did countless experiments with different kinds of igniters, worked on simple motor designs and methods of putting rockets together plus he provided many great ideas on rocketry in general. Much of that work is in this book. I want to thank Abdul M. Ismail who reviewed and helped edit the book. I would also like to thank the countless amateurs who have sent me e-mail or letters with tips on how to do things easier. I have incorporated many of those tips into this second edition so that other amateurs may benefit from them.

A special thank you for my wife, Martha. She put up with me while writing this book. She also did the running around necessary to get the book into reproduction, binding and distribution.

Finally, a big thank you to the men, women and children who come out to our local High Plains Rocketry Society launches. You will see some of their rockets in this book and video. I hope you will find a great bunch of fellow rocketeers like this in your area.

John Wickman

Author of
"How To Make Amateur Rockets"

Wickman Spacecraft & Propulsion Company

Mr. Wickman is currently developing a new launch vehicle under Air Force contract that uses an ammonium nitrate composite propellant. He was principal investigator on an Army contract to develop a pintle nozzle with integral thrust vector control for tactical missiles. He was the lead on the SHARP "S" Series sounding rocket launch team. The sounding rockets were to deploy scale prototype SHARP vehicles in Space for NASA Ames Research Center. The SHARP vehicles will conduct a series of aerodynamic maneuvers during each flight.

He was principal investigator on Phase I and II of a NASA Jet Propulsion Laboratory and Marshall Space Flight Center contract to develop rocket and jet engines that burn carbon dioxide with magnesium powder. This program was concluded successfully in 1998 with the delivery of the rocket and jet engines to NASA. In 1995, he was principal investigator on Phase I of the LOX/kerosene monopropellant rocket engine SBIR contract with the NASA Glenn Research Center. Mr. Wickman characterized LOX/kerosene monopropellant and test fired a small LOX/kerosene monopropellant rocket engine. In a previous SBIR contract, he demonstrated the feasibility of LOX/hydrocarbon monopropellants with shock sensitivity and combustion tests. The revolutionary idea of premixing liquid oxygen and hydrocarbons to form a safe liquid monopropellant could have a major impact on the future of liquid rocket engine technology.

Mr. Wickman has also served as principal investigator on a contract with NASA Glenn Research Center developing liquid oxygen/metal powder propellants that can be produced from elements commonly found on the moon. Other work performed by Mr. Wickman includes the design of subscale liquid oxygen monopropellant rocket engines, sounding rockets and small launch vehicles.

Mr. Wickman has conducted performance analyses continued the work of Dr. Adolf Oberth on various ammonium nitrate propellant formulations. Much of that work has been included in this book.

Mr. Wickman worked on the new Space Shuttle SRB field and nozzle joint designs for Morton

Thiokol under subcontract to Creare. This work included thermal analysis of the joint region with temperature predictions of the seals and metal parts and thermo-ablation predictions for the internal insulation. He has also presented to Thiokol engineers thermal design criteria for screening potential joint concepts. Mr. Wickman also worked with Chemical Systems Division of United Technologies on the Titan Recovery Program. This included thermal analysis for the test stand modification at the Air Force Phillips Laboratory for the vertical firing of Titan solid rocket boosters.

1974 - 1985: Aerojet Propulsion Company

In the Advanced Engineering group, Mr. Wickman performed air and ground launch missile systems design studies and trajectory analysis under subcontract to Rockwell for SCIBM and stand-off applications. He ran the Aerojet AIDE preliminary missile design computer code to determine missile length and weights. He has modified for Aerojet the AFAL MEMDOP trajectory computer code to include more accurate solid rocket design equations for missile design optimization.

Mr. Wickman was group leader of all thermal analysis in the company. This include the MX missile, Minuteman, Polaris and other tactical missile programs.

1972 - 1974: Pratt & Whitney Aircraft

Mr. Wickman worked on the thermal modeling and design of the burner section of the JT9D-70 engine used on large body aircraft. He was also responsible for the scheduling, design, testing and analysis of burner configurations in an experimental JT9D turbofan jet engine.

A Partial List Of Technical Publications

- Wickman, J.H, "In-Situ Mars Rocket and Jet Engines Burning Carbon Dioxide", AIAA 99-2409, 35th Joint Propulsion Conference, June 1999.
- Wickman, J.H., "Liquid Oxygen Monopropellants for Rocket Engines", AIAA 94-3173, 30th Joint Propulsion Conference, June 1994.
- Wickman, J.H., "Design of a LOX/Aluminum Lunar Propellant Rocket Engine", AIAA 94-2842, 30th Joint Propulsion Conference, June 1994.
- Wickman, J.H. and James, E., "Gelled Liquid Oxygen/Metal Powder Monopropellants", AIAA 92-3450, 28th Joint Propulsion Conference, June 1992.
- Wickman, J.H., Mockenhaupt, J.D. and Ditore, M.J., "An Investigation of Particle Impingement in Solid Rocket Nozzles", AIAA 79-1251, 15th Joint Propulsion Conference, June

Table of Contents

V. Flying Your Rocket

VI. Some Legal Issues Before You Fly

VII. Important Stuff!

Appendix

Amateur Rocketry - Past and Present

Introduction

Amateur rocketry is the foundation for all rocketry today whether it be professional, model rocketry or high power rocketry. The modern rocket's great ancestors were the amateur rockets built by the early pioneers of rocketry. These men had dreams of rockets taking people to the Moon, Mars and beyond. For the most part, they were considered crackpots who did not understand basic physics - *rockets cannot work in the vacuum of Space as there is nothing for the rocket exhaust to push against.* Of course, today we know that this is utter nonsense.

In the 1930's, these *crackpots* formed amateur rocketry societies to pool their financial resources and combine their skills to make successful rockets. These groups had names like "Verein fur Raumschiffahrt - VfR" (translation: Society for Space Travel) or the "American Interplanetary Society". The American Interplanetary Society later renamed itself the American Rocket Society (ARS) in an attempt to lessen chuckles and hoots from the establishment press and scientific/engineering community. The VfR had members like Wernher von Braun, Klaus Riedel and Willy Ley. The ARS had members like H. Franklin Pierce, Max Kraus, Edward Pendray and James Wyld. The ARS later became the professional society for aerospace engineers, The American Institute of Aeronautics and Astronautics or AIAA.

In the United States, many of the amateur rocketry societies were formed by universities and supervised by professors from the engineering college. However, there were a few groups and experimenters with no university affiliation. Most of the amateur groups closed down during World War II, but one of the groups that stay in operation was the Galcit Rocket Research Group. Galcit stood for Guggenheim Aeronautical Laboratory of the California Institute of Technology. Galcit formed in 1936 and was under the direction of Theodore von Karman with members like Frank Malina, Hsue-shen Tsien, Edward Forman, John Parsons and A.M.O. Smith.

During World War II, amateur rocketeers were recruited by Germany, Russia and the United States to develop rockets for military use. The V2 rocket drove home the point to political leaders on both sides of the ocean, that long range rockets were the weapons of the future. After the war, the old "amateur" rocketeers were enlisted by Russia and the United States to build missiles to carry nuclear warheads. With the launch of the Russian Sputnik satellite in the late 1950's, the *Great Space Race* was on, climaxing with the American Apollo 11 moon landing in 1969.

During 50's and 60's, amateur rocketeers across America were building rockets with about anything they could lay their hands on that would burn. With tremendous media support for America to take the lead in Space against Russia, these groups flourished in high schools and private schools. The organization of these groups was similar to the amateur groups of the 1930's. High school science teachers supervised the students on making rockets. The major guidebook was Capt. Brinley's, *Handbook of Amateur Rocketry*, published around 1960. The propellants of choice were zinc/sulfur or potassium nitrate mixed with melted sugar. The potassium nitrate/sugar propellant was called "Caramel Candy", although no one would recommend eating it.

These school groups, individual experimenters and old amateur rocketry societies had a good safety record. Unfortunately, with rocket fever gripping America, another group of individuals entered the amateur rocketry scene. They were soon to be known as the "Basement Bombers". In fairness to these people, many did not live in areas where they could join established amateur rocketry groups and learn. They also may not have been aware of amateur rocketry books that were available. For whatever reasons, it wasn't long before they started stuffing old CO_2 cartridges with match heads or black powder. Occasionally, this would result in a young person blowing off a hand or killing themselves which was widely reported in the media. Sometimes these people would be making fairly sophisticated rockets, but again, an accident would sometimes happen in the garage. Another explosion, fire or death which was given a lot of media play.

At this point, Estes Industries came on the stage with disposable and very reliable rocket motors. They also sold body tubes, fin material, nosecones, parachutes and all the things you needed to make small rockets. As a young boy in Jr. High School around 1962, I can remember getting Estes motors and making my own rockets. There was really no technical information regarding CP vs. CG or thrust to weight ratio, you were on your own. You learned by experimentation, but it was virtually impossible to seriously injure yourself with these motors or rockets. The Estes motors and supplies probably saved the lives and hands of many a budding aerospace engineer. Perhaps, even my own.

The success of Estes encouraged other companies to start producing model rocket motors and rocket kits. Even with commercial model rocket motors, high school amateur rocketry clubs were still going strong. My high school's club in Scottsdale, Arizona was still launching Carmel Candy rockets in 1967 when I graduated. Something happened after 1967, amateur rocketry societies and high school clubs began to disappear. A few rocketry societies remained and the high school clubs evolved into flying Estes rockets, but most amateurs went *underground.*

My personal opinion is that the drum beat of "you'll kill yourself if you make your rocket motors" was their undoing. Model rocketry organizations and commercial manufacturers led a major propaganda campaign to paint all amateur rocketeers as "basement bombers" The drum beat steadily during the 1970's until this *politically correct* message was firmly imbedded in the minds of all rocketeers, fire marshals and government officials. The few voices speaking out against this propaganda were not given much credibility. The old time amateur rocketeers of the 30's were now "professional" aerospace engineers and had no time or interest in the survival of amateur rocketry in America. Forgetting their roots, these engineers felt amateurs had nothing to contribute to "modern" rocketry, but bad publicity and accidents.

But, this is an introduction with a happy ending. Amateur rocketry is emerging from the dark ages of the past few decades. Technologies in the form of composite solid rocket propellants and the personal computer are responsible for the renaissance of amateur rocketeers. While the commercial manufacturers and model rocket organizations are still trying to suppress amateurs, they are losing the battle. NASA and aerospace industries are realizing that amateur rocketry lays the best foundation for aerospace engineering skills.

I would like to think that our initial CP Technologies booklets and our 1st Edition of "How To Make Amateur Rockets" played some part in helping along this renaissance. It was in that context that I decided to update this book with the latest information on making amateur rockets.

Basic Rocket Principals
Chapter 1

This is probably the most important chapter in the book. I would recommend you read this chapter several times until you really understand the concepts. Without getting lost in the long derivation of equations, I will focus on the principals of what makes a rocket work. The first set of principals involves the flight of the rocket. It is important to understand how a rocket flies before you design an engine for it. The second set explains how a rocket engine works. Once you understand these fundamental concepts, you will be able to design your rocket and its engine successfully regardless of whether it is solid, hybrid or liquid.

Rocket Flight

The basics of rocket flight are relatively simple. There are four forces acting upon the rocket, (1) gravity, (2) rocket engine thrust, (3) aerodynamic drag and (4) aerodynamic lift. The four forces are illustrated in Figure 1-1 for a rocket going through the atmosphere. The force of gravity is the weight of the rocket at any given time. The rocket engine thrust is the force produced by the rocket engine as it flies along. The aerodynamic drag is the force exerted on the rocket as it pushes through the atmosphere. The aerodynamic lift of the rocket is caused by an uneven pressure distribution on the outside of the rocket. This actually produces lift much like the wing of an airplane, although not nearly as efficient. For typical rockets, the aerodynamic lift can be neglected.

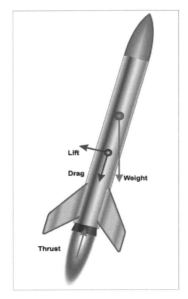

Figure 1-1: Forces Acting Upon a Rocket

Although it seems obvious, the thrust of the rocket engine must be greater than the weight of the rocket for it to get off the ground. I say obvious, but you would be surprised at the phone calls and emails I get from budding rocket scientists who design rockets with thrust less than the weight of the rocket. While the weight of the rocket is the greatest force the rocket engine must overcome at ignition, the aerodynamic drag force quickly eclipses this. The rocket will accelerate until the thrust of the rocket engine is exactly balanced by aerodynamic drag and weight. This is an important concept. The rocket will accelerate until its thrust is in balance with the weight and drag forces. Now, as the rocket climbs the air density decreases, so the rocket will increase slightly in velocity until the drag force again increases to bring all the forces in balance. In essence, the rocket is working mostly to push air rather than lift the rocket. If you are thinking about high altitude flights, remember this important concept. Don't waste propellant pushing air, use propellant to lift the rocket or overcome gravity.

Once the rocket is out of the atmosphere, the only force for the engine's thrust to balance is weight. In this case, it is more efficient to burn the propellant as quickly as possible to minimize the weight of propellant the rocket has to lift during the burn time. So, here is the second concept to remember. For upper stage rockets that are out of the atmosphere or essentially out of the atmosphere, you want to "pour it on" with respect to thrust. This of course will have to be within limits of the motor's chamber pressure and maximum acceleration limits of the rocket.

A useful concept in examining a rocket's flight path is its center of gravity. The force of gravity will pull on all parts of the rocket equally all around one point inside a rocket. This point is called the center of gravity or abbreviated as CG. A simple way to find the CG of your rocket is to find the point along your rocket where it balances. Do this in a room with no wind. A unique property of the center of gravity is that all of the forces shown in Figure 1-1 can be viewed as acting on the center of gravity. It is important to note, that while a rocket may wiggle or rotate, hopefully not do loops, and it will do all these things about the CG. The rocket may spin around the CG or rotate about the CG. The motion of the CG will be governed by thrust, drag, lift and weight of the rocket.

A trajectory calculation using this approach of only considering the motion of the CG and considering motion in all three directions of space is called a three dimensional (3D) trajectory simulation. If the motion is restricted to just altitude and a single downrange direction, it is two-dimensional or a 2D simulation. A simple straight up and straight down is a one-dimensional or 1D simulation. Of course in the real world, the rocket will spin (roll), point up or down (pitch) and point from side to side (yaw). More sophisticated trajectory simulations include all three of these motions as well and are called six dimensional or 6D trajectory simulations.

The simplest method of calculating the path of the rocket is to calculate the path of the rocket's CG with all forces acting on the CG. Let's take a 2D trajectory simulation where we will calculate the height of the rocket and the distance it goes downrange. The direction up will be called the "Y" direction and the distance downrange the "X" direction. We use Newton's law:

Force = (Mass) times (Acceleration) = M *A

Where:

Force = Summation of all the forces acting on the rocket such as thrust, drag, gravity (lbs)
M = Mass of the rocket at any given time (slugs) = (Weight of rocket at any given time)/(32.2)
A = Acceleration of the rocket in feet/second^2

To resolve the forces in the X and Y directions, we use some simple high school trigonometry. Forces in the X (to the right) and Y (up) directions will be considered positive. Forces acting in the opposite directions will be negative.

α is the angle the rocket is pointed and is measured from the horizon where 90 degrees is when the rocket is pointed straight up and 0 degree is when its pointed horizontal.

Forces (X) = (Thrust * cosine [α]) - (Drag * cosine [α])

Or:

Forces (X) = (Cosine [α]) * (Thrust - Drag)

In the Y-axis direction, the forces are as follows:

Forces (Y) = (Thrust * sine [α]) - (Drag * sine [α]) - (Rocket Weight)

Or:

Forces (Y) = {(Sine [α] * (Thrust - Drag)} - (Rocket Weight)

To calculate the movement of the center of gravity in each direction, we calculate the acceleration each direction.

Acceleration (X) = {Forces (X)]/[(Weight of Rocket/32.2)]
Acceleration (Y) = {Forces (Y)]/[(Weight of Rocket/32.2)]

Then we multiply the acceleration in each direction by a very small time increment to obtain the change in velocity during that time increment. The time increment we can call Delta T, which can be as large as 0.01 second. To obtain the actual velocity of the rocket, we add the change in velocity during the time increment to whatever the rocket's velocity was before the time increment. If we are just starting the calculation and the rocket is sitting on the pad, the old velocity will be zero. After the first time point calculation, the rocket will have some velocity. In that case, the old velocity will be equal to that velocity.

$$\text{Velocity (X)} = \text{Old Velocity (X)} + \{[\text{Acceleration (X)}] * [\text{Delta T}]\}$$
$$\text{Velocity (Y)} = \text{Old Velocity (Y)} + \{[\text{Acceleration (Y)}] * [\text{Delta T}]\}$$

The distance traveled in each direction during the Delta T time increment is given by:

$$\text{Distance (X)} = \text{Old Distance (X)} + (\{\text{Old Vel.(X)} + 0.5 * [\text{Accel. (X)}] * [\text{Delta T}]\} [\text{Delta T}])$$
$$\text{Distance (Y)} = \text{Old Distance (Y)} + (\{\text{Old Vel.(Y)} + 0.5 * [\text{Accel. (Y)}] * [\text{Delta T}]\} [\text{Delta T}])$$

We can keep track of the time during flight by the following:

$$\text{Time} = \text{Old Time} + \text{Delta T}$$

Now, to go through these equations using hand calculations for a typical rocket flight would be quite a chore. With personal computers, these calculations can be done in a few seconds. The included software program, FLIGHT, makes these calculations for you.

The values of the forces acting on the rocket can be determined at any time during the rocket's flight. The thrust can be obtained from measurements made on a thrust stand. The results are usually in the form of a curve or table of burn time versus thrust. It can also be obtained from theoretical calculations that will be discussed in Chapter 2 (liquid and hybrid engines) and Chapter 3 (solid rocket motors). The gravitational force on the rocket at any instant is simply its weight. The only change in weight during flight will be the loss of propellant while the rocket engine is burning. The weight of the rocket on the launch pad is the initial weight and the weight of the rocket after the rocket engine has completed its firing is called the burnout weight.

$$\text{Initial Weight} = W_i = \text{Weight of Rocket on Launch Pad}$$

$$\text{Burn-out Weight} = W_b = \text{Weight of Rocket After Engine is Done Firing}$$

$$\text{Burn-out Weight} = W_i - (\text{Weight of Propellant}) = W_i - W_p$$

If our rocket weighs 12 lbs on the launch pad and has two pounds of propellant, then the initial weight will equal 12 lbs and the burnout weight will equal 10 lbs (12 lbs - 2 lbs = 10 lbs). While the rocket engine is firing, the gravitational force on the rocket will start at 12 lbs and decrease to 10 lbs at engine cut-off.

The aerodynamic drag force may be calculated using fairly simple equations:

Aerodynamic drag = F_d = 0.5 * (Air Density) * C_d * (Frontal Area) * (Rocket's Speed)^2

Air Density = 0.075 exp.$(-7.4 \times 10^{-6} * h^{1.15})$ in lb/ft^3

Where:
h = Distance above sea level in feet.
Frontal Area = Largest cross-sectional area of the rocket

The main point when looking at these equations is that the rocket's speed through the air has a major impact on the drag force the rocket engine must overcome. The aerodynamic drag force the engine is working against is directly proportional to the speed squared. The drag force increases exponentially with the rocket's speed. To illustrate this, let's look at an example. Suppose our rocket is zipping along at 200 ft/second with a drag force of 40 lbs. If the rocket accelerates to 400 ft/second, only a doubling of the speed, the drag force increases to 160 lbs. The drag force doesn't just double; it goes up by a factor of four. Here's how to figure it out.

New Drag Force = (Old Drag Force) * [(New Speed)/(Old Speed)]^2

New Drag Force = 40 * [(400)/(200)]^2 = 40 * [2]^2 = 40 * 2 * 2 = 160 lbs

Suppose your rocket engine has a peak thrust of only 70 lbs, what do you think will happen in this case? Will it accelerate to 400 ft/second, which is equivalent to a drag force of 160 lbs? No, it won't because once it gets up to the point where the drag and gravity forces equal the thrust of the rocket engine, the rocket will stop accelerating. You can use this relationship to make a quick a calculation of the thrust required to propel a rocket to a given speed. If for your desired speed the drag force is 100 lbs, then your motor must generate 100 lbs of thrust plus the weight of the rocket. It must also generate this thrust level long enough for the rocket to accelerate to the desired speed.

Let's look at the other variables in the drag equation. The cross-sectional area of the rocket will be constant during flight unless there is staging to a different diameter or something is jettisoned during the flight to change the cross-sectional area. That leaves the drag coefficient or C_d. The drag coefficient relates the drag force to the shape of the rocket. If a flat board and a nosecone of the same cross-sectional area are going through air at the same speed and altitude, the drag force on each one will be different. The drag force on the nosecone will be much less than the drag force on the board, unless you have a pretty lousy nosecone. The drag coefficient takes the shape of the object into account and provides a correction factor to the drag force. Typical drag coefficients for different geometries are listed in Table 1-1.

Drag Coefficients for Different Shaped Objects
Table 1-1

Object	Length/Diameter	Cd
Square cylinder-perpendicular to flow	Infinitely Long	2.00
Circular cylinder-perpendicular to flow	5	0.35
Circular disk- perpendicular to flow	-	1.12
Rectangular flat plate-Normal to flow	1	1.10
"	5	1.20
"	20	1.50
"	Infinitely Large	2.00

The drag coefficient is handy since identically shaped objects will have the same drag coefficient even if the one of the objects is three times the size of the other. If we know the drag coefficient for a given shaped rocket, it will be the same regardless of the size of the rocket. For example, if we build a rocket with a three inch body tube that has a C_d of 0.50 and we scale everything up proportionately to a 12 inch body tube, the C_d will still be 0.50.

It should be noted that drag coefficient is not a constant with speed or aerodynamic angle of attack. Angle of attack is when the air is flowing past your rocket at an angle to the nosecone, rather than head-on. The influence of speed at zero angle of attack is shown for a V-2 rocket in Figure 1-2. For subsonic speeds, the drag coefficient is fairly constant until the rocket begins to approach the speed of sound or sonic speed. Then the drag coefficient climbs until it reaches a peak at about 1.2 and then decreases at higher speeds. This increase in the drag coefficient as the rocket approaches the speed of sound is present in other rocket geometries as well. This is another important concept to remember. As your rocket approaches Mach 1, not only will the drag force increase due to speed, but also due to an increase in the drag coefficient.

The next question on drag coefficients is, "What number should I use for my rocket?" Well, if your rocket is shaped like a V2, use Figure 1-2. For more conventionally shaped amateur rockets, the values shown in Figure 1-3 will probably be more appropriate. More drag

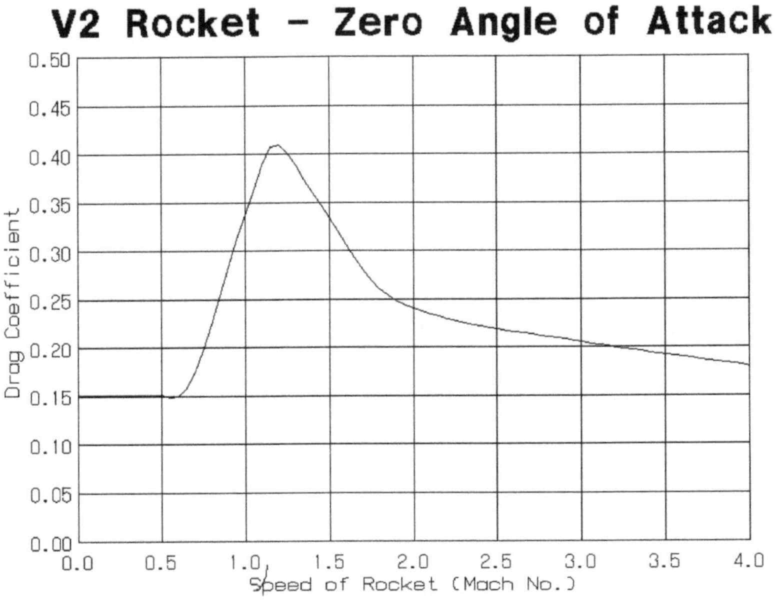

V2 Rocket – Zero Angle of Attack

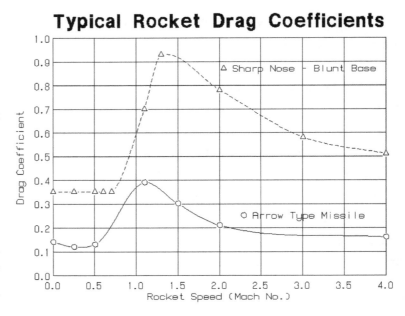

Figure 1-2: Drag Coefficient for V2 Rocket

coefficients for other shaped rockets are given in Appendix I. We have also included a great freeware program with this bookset called "Aerolab". It will calculate drag coefficients for your specific rocket geometry. I have compared it with more rigorous NASA programs and the correlation was excellent even at Mach numbers up to five.

Rocket Engines

Up to now, we have focused on gravity and aerodynamic forces on the rocket. But, the key force on the rocket comes from the rocket engine. Without this force, the rocket is not going anywhere. While there are all types of rocket engines, solid, liquid, hybrid, nuclear, ion, plasma and more, these rocket engines generate a force or thrust by ejecting mass at high speeds. In chemical engines (solid, liquid, hybrid), the mass is a gas, in nuclear

Typical Rocket Drag Coefficients

Figure 1-3: Typical Drag Coefficients for Amaateur Rockets

engines the mass is a gas or plasma and in ion engines it is ions. I guess that one is rather obvious. The important concept to get from the following discussion is that rocket engine thrust comes from the ejected mass multiplied by the velocity of the ejected mass. The ejected mass multiplied by the velocity of the ejected mass is called the momentum of the engine`s exhaust products. This momentum creates engine thrust and also imparts an impulse to the rocket engine.

Remember the Star Trek (Registered Trademark @ Paramount Studios) episodes where Scotty and the crew would talk about "simple impulse" engines? That`s where we are now. All our rocket engines are simple impulse engines. Warp drive was not an impulse engine. You will have to wait for a future edition of this bookset to learn about "warp drives".

This brings us to another important concept to remember. The total impulse of the engine is equal to the momentum of the ejected mass from the engine or the average thrust multiplied by the total burn time. Total impulse is always expressed in force-time units. Often total impulse is expressed in metric units of Newton-seconds where Newtons is substituted for pounds.

Ejected Mass Momentum = Total Impulse = (Mass of propellant) * (Propellant Ejection Velocity)

The total impulse provided by a rocket engine is also equal to its thrust multiplied by the time the thrust is present. For variable thrust engines, it is the area under the thrust-time curve. The total impulse of an engine is used in model and high power rocketry to classify the engine by a letter grade. The total impulse of an engine can be expressed as the average thrust multiplied by the total engine burn time.

Impulse = I = (Average Thrust) * (Total Burn Time) = $F_{avg} * t_b$

Where:
F_{avg} = Average Thrust
t_b = Total Burn Time

For example, if we have an engine with an average thrust of 20 lbs for 6 seconds duration, the total impulse would be 120 lbs-seconds (20 lbs multiplied by 6 seconds = 120 lbs-seconds).

Relating these two expressions for the same quantity, total impulse, we get:

Total Impulse = I = (Average Thrust) * (Burn Time) = (Mass of propellant) * (Propellant Ejection Velocity)

Now, if we divide the above equation by the burn time, an expression for the thrust results.

Average Thrust = Favg = (Propellant Mass Flowrate) * (Propellant Ejection Velocity)

Propellant Mass Flowrate = (Mass of Propellant) / (Burn Time)

It is important to note that we are talking about the mass of propellant, not weight. In English units, the weight of something is expressed in pounds, while the mass is expressed in slugs. Pounds are converted into slugs by dividing the weight in pounds by 32.2. The number 32.2 is usually expressed in equations as g. So that:

Mass of Propellant = M_p = (Weight of Propellant)/(32.2)

While we may calculate the average propellant mass flowrate by dividing the mass of propellant by the burn time, the value for the ejection velocity is not immediately obvious. However a special parameter will enable us to easily calculate the ejection velocity. This parameter is called Specific Impulse or Isp. It is defined for all rocket engines as the propellant ejection velocity divided by g or 32.2 in English units:

Specific Impulse = Isp = (Propellant Ejection Velocity)/32.2

If we combine this definition of specific impulse with the earlier equation for average thrust, we come up with an extremely useful equation in designing rocket engines:

Average Thrust = Favg = (Propellant Weight Flowrate) * Isp

Or

Propellant Weight Flowrate = (Average Thrust) / Isp

Or

Isp = (Average Thrust) / (Propellant Weight Flowrate)

These expressions are very powerful and you should remember them. Let`s take a couple of examples to illustrate how useful they are. Suppose someone gives you a motor design that has 2 lbs of propellant and burns for 10 seconds with a specific impulse of 200 seconds. What is the average thrust? Simple! Divide the weight of propellant by the burn time to get the propellant weight flowrate, which is 2 lbs divided by 10 seconds to yield 0.2 lbs/seconds. Multiple that by the specific impulse of 200 seconds to get an average thrust of 40 lbs.

$$F_{avg} = [(2 \text{ lbs}) / (10 \text{ seconds})] * 200 \text{ seconds} = 40 \text{ lbs of thrust}$$

Suppose you want a motor with an average thrust of 25 lbs at a specific impulse of 220 seconds, what is the propellant weight flowrate? Divide the thrust of 25 lbs by the specific impulse of 220 seconds to get 0.114 lbs/second. How useful is that number? Well, if you want to make that motor have a duration of 10 seconds, then multiply the propellant weight flowrate by the total burn time, which is 0.114 lbs/second multiplied by 10 to get 1.14 lbs. So I would need 1.14 lbs of propellant for a motor with a specific impulse of 220 seconds, a duration of 10 seconds and an average thrust of 25 lbs.

Finally, you make a motor that has 5 lbs of propellant, burns for 10 seconds and has an average thrust of 120 lbs. You want to know what the specific impulse of your motor is so you can brag to your buddies. The propellant weight flowrate is 5 lbs divided by 10 seconds to yield 0.5 lbs/second. Dividing the propellant weight flowrate of 0.5 lbs/second into the average thrust of 125 lbs yields 250 seconds. Hey, I'm impressed!

As you can see this simple relationship between thrust, weight of propellant, burn time and specific impulse will permit you to get an immediate idea if the motor you want to design is even possible. As we will find out in Chapter 4, propellants are only capable of delivering so much specific impulse no matter how efficiently they are used. If you want a motor to deliver 300 lbs of thrust for 10 seconds that only requires 5 lbs of propellant, forget it. You need a propellant that delivers a specific impulse of 600 seconds. This is well beyond chemical propulsion and would be well into the nuclear propulsion area.

If at maximum chamber pressure, your propellant formulation can deliver 240 seconds of specific impulse, then you would require a propellant flowrate of 0.3125 lbs/second to obtain a thrust level of 75 lbs. If your chamber can only hold 1.5 lbs of propellant, then your burn time can only be 4.8 seconds (1.5 lbs divided by 0.3125 lbs/second = 4.8 seconds).

Adjustments For Those Who Must Be Technical About It

I should note that when the propellant is exhausted as a gas out of an exit cone, a correction must be applied to the propellant ejection or exhaust velocity. In a typical chemical rocket engine, the propellant burns and exits the engine as a gas through an exit cone into the atmosphere. The gas starts at the pressure inside the chamber and then decreases in pressure as it flows through the nozzle throat and then out the exit cone. If the pressure of the gas is the same as the pressure of the atmosphere when it leaves the exit cone, no correction is necessary. But, if it is different and it almost always is, then a correction must be applied.

The reason for the correction is due to a difference in the atmospheric pressure and the gas pressure at the end of the exit cone. If the exit cone gas pressure is lower than the pressure of the atmosphere, then the end of the exit cone will produce a negative thrust, which must be accounted for. Consequently, the thrust equation is rewritten as follows:

Average Thrust = F_{avg} = (Propellant Mass Flowrate) * (Propellant Gas Exhaust Velocity) + [Exit Cone Cross-Sectional Area * (Exit Cone Exhaust Pressure - Atmospheric Pressure)]

$$\text{Average Thrust} = Favg = [M_p * u_e] + [A_e * (P_e - P_a)]$$

As you can see if the exit cone pressure equals the atmospheric pressure, then the thrust equation simplifies to what we had previously. If the exit cone pressure is less than atmospheric, then the last term is negative and reduces the thrust level. If the exit cone pressure is greater than the atmospheric pressure, then the term is positive and initially appears to increase thrust, but this is misleading. In this situation, the exhaust velocity is reduced so that the thrust is actually lower. The optimum condition or maximum thrust is obtained when the exit cone exhaust pressure is equal to atmospheric pressure.

So that we can still use the previously simple equations for thrust and specific impulse, an equivalent exhaust velocity is defined as:

Equivalent Velocity = Ueq = Exit Cone Gas Velocity + [Exit Cone Cross-Sectional Area * (Exit Cone Pressure - Atmospheric Pressure) / Propellant Mass Flow Rate)

$$\text{Equivalent Velocity} = U_{eq} = U_e + [A_e * (P_e - P_a)/m_p)]$$

Then the specific impulse is defined as:

$$\text{Specific Impulse} = Isp = \text{Equivalent Velocity} / 32.2 = U_{eq} / 32.2 = U_{eq}/g$$

As you can see, when the exit pressure equals the atmosphere pressure ($P_e = P_a$), then the specific impulse is equal to the exit velocity of the propellant divided by 32.2 as we mentioned earlier. Ok, now the technically correct people should be satisfied. Let's move on.

Characteristic Velocity

I know your head may feel like exploding with the equations so far, but hang on for a few more pages. There is a parameter known as the characteristic velocity or C*. This relates the propellant exhaust velocity without considering the effects of the exit cone. It can be expressed as follows:

$$C^* = \text{Square Root } \{[(R^*T)/(\gamma)]^*[(\gamma+1)/2]^{[(\gamma+1)/(\gamma-1)]}\}$$

Where:
γ = ratio of specific heats = C_p / C_v
R = (Universal gas constant) / (molecular weight of the propellant gas)
T = Propellant gas temperature in the chamber

The characteristic velocity is really just dependent on the propellant formulation and gas temperature. It can be calculated for your propellant formulation using the CHEM software included with this book. As shown in Figure 1-4, it is a fairly weak function of chamber pressure because chamber pressure hardly affects gamma and the gas temperature. This weak dependency makes C* useful for calculating the chamber pressure if you know the throat area and propellant weight flow rate. The chamber pressure can be calculated with the following expression:

Chamber Pressure (psi) = [(Propellant weight flowrate) * (C*)]/[(Throat Area)*32.2]

Where the propellant weight flowrate in lbs/second, C* in ft/second and throat area in inch².

This is another equation to re-member, as you will soon see why. Suppose we have a motor with a characteristic velocity of 4500 ft/second, the throat area is 0.11 inch²

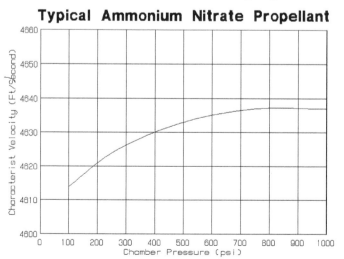

Figure 1-4: C* change with Chamber Pressure

reflecting a throat diameter of 0.375 inches and a propellant weight flowrate of 0.2 lbs/second. We can then calculate the chamber pressure as:

Chamber pressure = (0.2 * 4500)/(0.11 * 32.2) = 900/3.542 = 254 psi

We can modify this equation to determine the required throat area for a desired chamber pressure with a given propellant weight flowrate and C*. Let`s take the previous example and calculate the throat area for a desired chamber pressure of 700 psi. We can use the following equation:

Throat area (inch²) = (Propellant weight flowrate) * (C*)/[(Chamber Pressure)*32.2]

Throat area = (0.2 * 4500)/(700 * 32.2) = 900/22540 = 0.04 inch²

We can convert this to a throat diameter using the following relationship:

Throat Diameter (Inches) = Square Root [1.274 * (Throat Area)] = Square Root[1.274*0.04]

Throat Diameter (Inches) = Square Root [0.051] = 0.23 inches

So we would need a throat diameter of 0.23 inches to get a chamber pressure of 700 psi with this propellant formulation and propellant weight flowrate. Regardless of whether the engine is liquid, hybrid or solid, I can easily calculate chamber pressure knowing throat area, C* and propellant weight flow rate. The throat area is a design parameter and C* comes from the propellant chemistry. For liquid engines, the propellant weight flow rate is also a design parameter or directly controlled. For solids and hybrids, it is a function of other parameters, which we will get into in the next chapter.

Now, if I know the chamber pressure, I can calculate thrust directly using the following equation. This new equation introduces the final key parameter, the thrust coefficient.

Thrust = (Chamber Pressure) * (Throat Area) * (Nozzle Coefficient) = $P_c * A_t * C_f$

Thrust Coefficient

The thrust coefficient is a multiplying factor reflecting the momentum generated by the exhaust. It is a function of the propellant formulation (actually, its gas constant), but to a greater extent it is dependent on the throat area to exit area of the cone or the ratio of chamber pressure to atmospheric pressure. The equation for the thrust coefficient is listed below for the case of a motor having an exit cone and not having an exit cone.

$$C_f = \text{Square root } \{[(2\gamma^2)/(\gamma-1)]*[1-(p_e/p_c)^{[(\gamma-1)/\gamma]}]*[2/(\gamma+1)]^{[(\gamma+1)/(\gamma-1)]}\}+\{[(P_e-P_a)/P_c]*(A_e/A_t)\}$$

$$C_f \text{ (No exit cone) } = \text{Square root } \{\gamma^2 * [2/(\gamma+1)]^{[(2*\gamma)/(\gamma-1)]}\} + [2/(\gamma+1)]^{[\gamma/(\gamma-1)]} - P_a/P_c$$

Where:
γ = ratio of specific heats = C_p / C_v
A_e = cross-sectional area of exit cone at its end
A_t = cross-sectional area of the nozzle throat
P_a = ambient pressure (psia)
P_c = chamber pressure (psia)
P_e = pressure at end of exit cone (psia)

Don't be overwhelmed by the equations. You don't have to calculate these values as that is done for you in FPRED. Also, Appendix H has a list of values for C_f that is given in tabular form. The important thing to know is that with a C* value, a throat area and the weight flowrate of the propellant, you can calculate the thrust of the motor.

Using our previous example, suppose we want to calculate the thrust of the motor. To determine the thrust coefficient using the table in Appendix H, we can determine the atmospheric pressure to chamber pressure ratio. At sea level, the atmospheric pressure is 14.7 psia. Notice the "a" after "psi", that means "absolute". The chamber pressure must be converted from 700 psi to psia. That is done by always adding 14.7 to it. So the chamber pressure is 714.7 psia.

$$psia = psi + 14.7$$

The exit pressure to chamber pressure ratio is then:

$$p_e/p_c = (14.7)/(714.7) = 0.02057$$

From the table in Appendix H, we look for the closest match to 0.02057 under the p_e/p_c column until we find 0.020778. Go across to the C_{fopt} column and read off the value of 1.51419. Then, we would use the following equation to determine the thrust:

Thrust (lbs) = Chamber Pressure * Throat Area * C_f

Thrust (lbs) = (700) * (0.04) * (1.51419) = 42.397 lbs

You will also note in the table the column "ε" which stands for exit cone expansion ratio. The value for our case is 6.5. This means the ratio of the exit cone exit diameter divided by the throat diameter squared is equal to 6.5.

$$\varepsilon = (\text{exit cone exit diameter/throat diameter})^2 = 6.5$$

Exit cone exit diameter = (throat diameter) * (Square Root [6.5]) = 0.23 * 2.55 = 0.59

So, to achieve a C_f of 1.51419, we need an exit cone diameter of 0.59 inches.

Hybrid and Liquid Rocket Engines
Chapter 2

In the previous chapter, we learned the fundamentals of rocket engines whether they are chemical or some other type. In this chapter, we are going to focus on chemical rocket engines and more specifically, hybrid and liquid rocket engines.

Liquid Rocket Engines

Liquid rocket engines inject two or more liquid propellants into a combustion chamber. Usually, the liquids are stored inside tanks, which are located in the fuselage of the rocket. A notable exception to this is the Space Shuttle where the liquid propellants are stored inside an External Tank. The liquid propellants are either transferred to the combustion chamber by means of pumps or a pressurized gas that forces the liquids out of the tank. Based on the propellant feed system, liquid propulsion systems are usually referred to as pump-fed or pressure-fed, Figure 2-1. Liquid rocket systems are probably the most difficult propulsion systems for the amateur to make and any amateur who makes a successful pump-fed liquid propulsion system is no amateur in my book. If amateurs venture into the liquid propulsion arena, it is usually with a pressure-fed system. To produce turbines and pumps is beyond their budget and facilities.

In most liquid propulsion systems, the oxidizer and fuel are kept in separate tanks. As the name suggests, the oxidizer provides the oxygen to burn the fuel. Some oxidizers and fuels used in industry are listed in Table 2-1.

Performance of Typical Liquid Propellants
Table 2-1

Fuel	Oxidizer	Specific Impulse (Seconds) @ 400 psi & Sea Level Expansion
Hydrazine	Nitrogen Tetroxide	250
Hydrazine	Oxygen	265
Hydrazine	Red Fuming Nitric Acid	247
Hydrogen	Fluorine	390
Hydrogen	Oxygen	360
JP-4	Oxygen	247
Kerosene	Oxygen	240

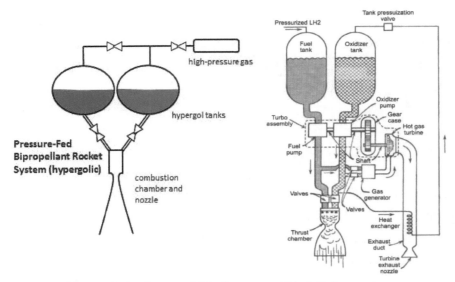

Figure 2-1: Gas and Turbopump Feed Schematics

To propel the oxidizer and fuel out of their respective tanks, an inert gas is used to push them out and down the feed lines running to the combustion chamber. The inert gas is usually nitrogen or helium. The inert gases will be in a storage tank, which is at a very high pressure. If this pressurized gas were fed directly to the propellant tanks, the propellants would be expelled into the feed lines at too great of a speed. To solve this problem a gas regulator is connected to the inert gas tank to reduce the pressure of the gas feeding to the oxidizer and fuel tanks.

An on-off valve is usually installed between the inert gas tank and the propellant tanks. This can be a single valve with a T-fitting splitting the gas between the oxidizer and fuel tanks. Downstream of each fuel and oxidizer tank in the feed line to the combustion chamber is an on-off valve and a throttling valve or throttling orifice. The on-off valve is turned to on to permit the fuel or oxidizer to flow to the combustion chamber. The throttling valve or throttling orifice controls the mass flow rate of the oxidizer or fuel so that the desired mixture ratio is obtained in the combustion chamber.

The most difficult part of designing a liquid rocket engine is the injector. It must atomize

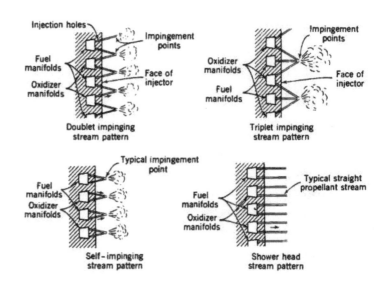

Figure 2-2: Typical Liquid Injectors

the liquid into droplets plus mix the fuel and oxidizer for good combustion. It is desirable to do this in as short a length as possible to minimize the weight of the combustion chamber and heat loading inside the chamber. The problem is that when the propellants are shot into the chamber, they are racing towards the throat at the same time they are atomizing, mixing and burning. If the propellant burns outside of nozzle, the thrust from the propellant will be lost. Some typical injector patterns are shown in Figure 2-2.

Let`s take a look at some of the calculations you may make in designing a simple liquid rocket engine. First, you need to select your fuel and oxidizer, the desired chamber pressure and mixture ratio. You can use CHEM to run a variety of chamber pressures and mixture ratios, using Isp as a measure of performance. The highest Isp is probably the one you want to pick. For practical matters, the chamber pressure in a pressure fed system should be moderately low. I would recommend going no higher than 400 psi and you may want to shoot for something around 250 psi. From CHEM you will get the C* for the chamber pressure, mixture ratio and propellant combination you select.

Suppose we want to design a LOX/kerosene (J4) rocket engine with a 250 psi chamber pressure, a mixture ratio of 70% oxygen and 30% kerosene and producing a thrust of 200 lbs at sea level conditions. From CHEM, I obtain all the key performance parameters necessary.

LOX = ID number 749
J4 (basically kerosene) = ID number 563.

Key output:

- Chamber Pressure: 250 psi
- Exit pressure: 14.7 psia
- Chamber Temperature = 5761 F
- Gamma = 1.224
- Molecular Weight = 22.19
- C* = 5726 ft/second

We can obtain the value for C_f using the C_f table in Appendix H knowing the gamma and the pressure ratio which is (14.7/[250+14.7]) = 0.0555. From the table we see that C_f is approximately = 1.538 and the expansion ratio is approximately 3.2.

Remember from Chapter 1, the thrust is:

$$\text{Thrust} = P_c * A_t * C_f$$

We can solve this for throat area:

$$A_t = (\text{Thrust})/(C_f * P_c) = (200 \text{ lbs})/(1.538 * 250 \text{ psi}) = 0.520 \text{ inch}^2$$

Throat diameter = Square root $[(4 * A_t)/3.14]$ = Square root $(2.08/3.14)$ = 0.81 inches

So, we now know the throat diameter and we can calculate the propellant weight flow rate using from Chapter 1:

$$\text{Propellant weight flowrate} = [(P_c * A_t * 32.2) / C*$$

$$W_p = (250 * 0.52 * 32.2) / (5726) = 4186/5726 = 0.731 \text{ lbm/second}$$

This is the combined propellant flow rate of fuel and oxidizer. For the individual oxygen and J4 weight flow rates we can calculate as follows:

$$\text{Oxygen } W_p = 0.70 * 0.731 = 0.5117 \text{ lbm/second}$$

$$\text{J4 } W_p = 0.30 * 0.731 = 0.2193 \text{ lbm/second}$$

The next step is to size the injector holes. We can use the following formula as a starting point:

Oxidizer or fuel weight flowrate = (Density of Liquid) * (Total Injector Hole Area) * (12 * Injection Velocity)

<u>Or</u>

Total Injector Hole Area = (Oxidizer or fuel weight flowrate) / [12 * (Density of Liquid) * (Injection Velocity)]

The injection velocity can be calculated with the following formula:

Injection velocity = (Discharge Coefficient) * square root {2 * 32.2 * (Pressure Drop Across Injector)/[(Density of Liquid) * 12.0]}

<u>Where:</u>

Pressure Drop = Pressure Drop across the injector (psi)

Density of Liquid = Density of liquid oxidizer or fuel lbm/in³

The discharge coefficient depends on the type of injector. If the injector consists of short tubes with rounded inlets, the discharge coefficient could be as high as 0.97 to 0.99. For sharp cornered tubes or orifices, the discharge coefficient is typically 0.6 to 0.8. The pressure drop across the injector should be at least 50 psi. Usually, the higher the pressure drop the better atomization of the liquid out of the injector.

Suppose for our engine, we pick a pressure drop of 100 psi and use orifices so that the discharge coefficient is 0.70. We can calculate the injection velocity first for the liquid oxygen. From the full CHEM output, we see that the density of the LOX is 0.0412 lbm/in3. Then the injection velocity for the LOX is:

Injection velocity LOX = 0.7 * square root [(2 * 32.2 * 100)/(0.0412 * 12)]

Injection velocity LOX = 0.7 * square root [6440/0.4944] = 0.7 * 114.13 = 79.89 ft/second

The LOX injector area = (0.5117) / (12 * 0.0412 * 79.89) = 0.5117 / 39.50 = 0.01295 in²

The individual hole areas can be determined by the following:

Hole Area = (Injector Area) / (Number of Holes)

If we select five holes for the LOX, then each hole has an area of:

LOX Hole Area = 0.01295 / 5 = 0.00259 in²

<u>Or</u>

LOX Hole Diameter = square root [(4 * Hole Area)/3.14] = square root (0.01036/3.14) = 0.05744 inches

So, we will need five holes for the LOX with each hole at 0.05744 inches in diameter, slightly smaller than a 1/16th hole. The same procedure is used to find the hole diameter for the J4 fuel.

Once the number of holes and hole size for the fuel and oxidizer are calculated, the next question is, "How big should the combustion chamber be?" The combustion chamber size is based on a parameter called the characteristic length of the chamber denoted as L*. It is also dependent on the Mach number of the combustion gases inside the chamber. The lower the Mach number, the longer the fuel and oxidizer droplets stay inside the chamber and the more likely that complete combustion will occur. Essentially, the bigger the chamber, the more complete combustion is obtained in the engine.

To keep engine weight down, it is desired to have as small a chamber as possible while still maintaining good combustion efficiency. Keeping the Mach between 0.05 and 0.10 inside the chamber can typically do this. We can use the isentropic gas laws to determine the area of the combustion chamber to the area of the throat for the desired Mach number. Suppose we select an internal Mach number 0.05 for the combustion chamber. For a gamma of 1.22, we can use Appendix M to obtain the area ratio. A Mach number 0.05 has an area ratio of 11.86. Then:

$$A_c/A_t = 11.86$$

$$D_c/D_t = \text{square root } (A_c/A_t) = \text{square root } (11.86) = 3.44$$

$$D_c = 3.44 * D_t = 3.44 * 0.81 = 2.79 \text{ inches}$$

So, the chamber diameter should be 2.79 inches in diameter. The last chamber parameter to determine is the length. This can be done using the "Characteristic Length" or L*. Some values for different propellant combinations are given in Table 2-1.

$$L* = (\text{Chamber volume}) / (\text{Throat Area})$$

Unfortunately, the values for LOX and J4 are not listed in the table. However, due to the longer time for J4 to vaporize compared to alcohol, we can expect the L* value to be larger than for LOX and alcohol. As a starting point, we may want to try L* equals 75 inches.

<u>Then:</u>

$$\text{Chamber Volume} = 75 \text{ inches} * 0.52 \text{ inches} = 39 \text{ inches}^3$$

$$\text{Chamber Length} = (\text{Chamber Volume}) / ([3.14/4] * D_c^2) = (39) / ([3.14/4] * [2.79^2])$$

Chamber Length = 39.0 / 6.11 = 6.38 inch

Typical L* values for different propellant systems at 300 psia
Table 2-1

Propellant System	L* (Inches)
LOX - Hydrogen	10
Nitric Acid - Aniline	40
Nitric Acid - Gasoline	50
LOX - Alcohol	50

As this was an estimate based on a minimum L* value, this chamber length will probably be too short. By testing the engine and measuring the C* combustion efficiency, it can be determined if combustion chamber is too short and needs to be lengthened. The nozzle and exit cone design are done using the procedures discussed in Chapter 1.

In designing your engine, you will need to first consider whether you want to work with cryogenic propellants. Cryogenic LOX must be handled with extreme care, as it will form explosives with many materials on contact. The extreme cold temperatures also require special materials that maintain strength at cryogenic temperatures and valves that do not freeze up. Having worked with cryogenic propellants for several years, they are a major pain to work with which is why industry is always searching for new room-temperature propellants. The room temperature propellants are fine with respect to working temperature. Unfortunately, most of them have extremely toxic fumes

Recently, amateurs have been experimenting with a new liquid oxidizer, nitrous oxide. While it is actually a gas in it's natural state, under pressure it can be drawn as a liquid from a tank. Nitrous oxide also has the advantage of being self-pressurizing. Since it is relatively safe, amateurs in the future may be using it with kerosene or alcohol to make liquid rocket engines.

Hybrid Rocket Engines

Hybrid rocket engines are what the name suggests, a combination of solid and liquid propellants. As mentioned earlier, a liquid rocket engine uses all liquid propellants. Solid rocket motors consist of solid chemicals, which have been cast into the combustion chamber.

In hybrid engines, either the fuel or oxidizer is cast as a solid into the combustion chamber. The other propellant is sprayed into the chamber for combustion to take place. Usually, the fuel is cast into the chamber while the oxidizer is sprayed in as a liquid.

Hybrids saw a major renaissance in the 1980's due to the emergence of the American Rocket Company. They were first company to privately develop a large hybrid rocket engine and demonstrate it on test stands at Edward's Air Force base. The oxidizer was liquid oxygen and the fuel was essentially HTPB which is the binder used in most Space booster solid propellants. Unfortunately, their "first flight" rocket caught fire on the launch pad due to a partially stuck open LOX valve. Although, the company made a valiant effort to recover from this fire, investors in the company were scared away and in the early 1990's, the company closed its doors for good. Hybrids can be looked at as combining the best of solids and liquids or the worst. Probably both viewpoints are true.

Hybrids have found their way into the high power rocketry arena in the 1990's. Two companies, Aerotech and Hypertech, are selling complete systems to consumers in the United States. These systems use nitrous oxide as the oxidizer with various fuel grains depending on the motor and manufacturer. When the rocket containing the hybrid rocket engine is not loaded with the oxidizer, it is safe, non-explosive and non-flammable. This has major advantages from a regulatory and transportation standpoint. This was a major reason for its introduction into high power rocketry. Amateurs have also been experimenting with hybrids using either nitrous oxide or LOX as the oxidizer. Fuels have ranged from paper phenolic, HTPB binder, asphalt, plastic and just about anything that is castable and flammable.

The basic operation of a hybrid rocket engine is fairly easy. Typically, a fuel grain is cast into a combustion chamber. By itself, the fuel grain will not burn since there is no oxidizer present to support the combustion process. The oxidizer is either self-pressurizing as in the case of nitrous oxide or is pressurized with another gas as is the case for LOX. A valve between the oxidizer tank and the combustion chamber controls the flow of oxidizer and thus provides a method of throttling the engine. The more oxidizer, the more combustion which increases the thrust of the engine. The less oxidizer and the less combustion resulting in lower thrust. When the oxidizer valve is opened, an ignition source is set off inside the combustion chamber to ignite the fuel grain. The oxidizer tank is a few hundred psi above the combustion chamber pressure for steady combustion. The major challenge for the hybrid engine is mixing the fuel and oxidizer to the proper mixture ratio. Since the oxidizer comes into the chamber at the forward end, the combustion process is oxidizer rich at the forward end, about right in the middle and oxidizer lean at the aft end.

To design your own hybrid rocket engine, the procedure is similar to designing a liquid rocket engine. You need to pick a fuel and oxidizer combination, run it on CHEM2 to determine performance and selected the chamber pressure and throat area. The oxidizer injection holes are calculated the same way as for a liquid engine.

The fuel is not directly injected as with a liquid engine, but is injected into the combustion chamber based on the exposed surface area of the cast fuel grain, fuel ablation rate and the density of the fuel grain. It can be expressed by the following expression:

Weight of hybrid fuel injection = (A_{fuel}) * (Fuel Density) * (Fuel Ablation Rate)

A_{fuel} = Surface area of fuel grain

The fuel ablation rate is given by:

Fuel Ablation Rate (Inch/second) = $r_f = c * G^n$

c = empirical ablation coefficient
n = empirical ablation exponent
G = Oxidizer mass velocity (lb/in^2 - second)

G = (Oxidizer Weight Flow)/(Combustion Port Area)

The combustion port area is the cross-sectional area of bore where combustion is taking place. Assuming the fuel grain has a single bore of 0.5 inches in diameter down its length, then the Combustion Port Area would be:

Combustion Port Area = (3.14/4) * (Diameter)^2 = (0.785) * (0.5)^2 = (0.785) * (0.25)

Combustion Port Area = 0.19625 in^2

The oxidizer weight flow would be calculated based on the total propellant weight flow and the mixture ratio as was done with liquid propellants. Unfortunately, the constants, c, n and m must be determined by experimentation. They are dependent on the fuel and oxidizer, the oxidizer flow rate and pressure of combustion. The easiest way to determine these constants is to run a series of motor tests where the oxidizer mass velocity is varied over the range of interest for your particular motor design for the selected fuel and oxidizer. Plot the regression rate of the fuel grain versus the oxidizer mass velocity on Log - Log paper. The data points will form a straight line. The slope of the line is the exponent n. The coefficient, c, is determined by picking a regression rate and the corresponding oxidizer mass flow rate. For example, suppose the exponent is 0.45 and an oxidizer flow rate of 0.40 lbm/in^2-second gives a fuel regression rate of 0.3 in/seconds. Then:

$$0.3 \text{ inches/second} = c * (0.40)^{0.45} = c * 0.662$$

We can solve for c by dividing 0.3 by 0.662 to yield:

$$c = 0.3/0.662 = 0.453$$

The final parameter to determine in the hybrid engine is the fuel grain size. For a straight bore, the fuel surface area is:

$$A_{fuel} = [2 * (3.14/4) * (OD^2 - BD^2)] + [3.14* (\text{Fuel Length}) * (BD)]$$

BD = Burning Bore Diameter as a function of time
OD = Outer diameter of the fuel grain
Fuel length = Length of the fuel grain as a function of time.

At time zero, BD will be equal to the inside bore diameter. At end of firing when all the fuel has been consumed, BD will equal the outer diameter of the fuel grain, OD. Note, the fuel length will be getting shorter as the ends of the fuel grain burn back.

The trick in designing the fuel grain is to get the fuel flow rate to be what you want to match the oxidizer flow rate. The example used the simplest fuel grain pattern, a simple cylinder with a bore. You can use more complicated geometries to get the desired flow rate.

Solid Rocket Motors
Chapter 3

Solid rocket motors were probably the earliest rocket motors with the invention of black powder. The powder was packed into the rocket chambers in a conical pattern to produce a high thrust with a duration. Their attractiveness stemmed from their simplicity. Just ignite the powder and away they went. The major drawback to these early solid motors was their low performance with respect to specific impulse. Also, they were somewhat unreliable due to cracks in the propellant grains. During the early days of rocketry, Goddard, Von Braun and Oberth, focused on liquid propellants due to their higher performance and controllability. Solid rocket motors received serious consideration for Space launches and missile applications with the wide spread use of composite propellants in the 1950's. The major advantage of composite solid rocket propellants for the amateur is the simplicity of the design, reliability, good performance and safety.

The solid rocket motor works on the same principals as liquids and hybrid rocket engines. Both the fuel and oxidizer are injected into the chamber and burned with the hot gases going out the nozzle. The major difference is that in a solid rocket motor, the fuel and oxidizer are premixed in the right proportions and cast inside the rocket chamber. The propellant weight flow rate injected into the rocket chamber is solely dependent on the propellant density, propellant surface area and burn rate of the propellant. Since the propellant density is usually a constant during the burn of the motor, the propellant weight flow rate is really controlled by the propellant surface area and burn rate.

Propellant weight flow rate = W_p = (Propellant Density) * (Propellant Surface Area) * (Propellant Burn Rate)

The propellant surface area is dependent on the propellant grain pattern. The grain pattern is the geometric shape of the solid propellant in the rocket chamber, Figure 3-1. These basic patterns can be combined with others or varied to form many different patterns. The idea is that as the propellant burns, the surface area changes to increase, remain constant or decrease. This is the first tool the motor designer has to control propellant weight flow rate.

The second tool is the propellant burn rate. Each propellant formulation burns at a different rate for a given pressure. For a specific burn area, the designer can pick a propellant formulation that gives a burn rate so that the propellant weight flow rate is the desired one. The burn rate is determined experimentally for each propellant formulation and given by the following formula:

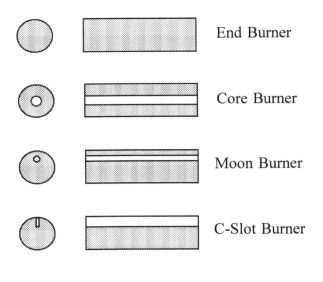

End Burner

Core Burner

Moon Burner

C-Slot Burner

Figure 3-1: Typical Propellant Grain Patterns

Propellant Burn Rate = $c * P_c^n$

c = Burn rate coefficient
n = Burn rate exponent
P_c = Chamber pressure

The third tool for the solid rocket motor designer is throat diameter. Most solid rocket motors use a nozzle material that erodes as the propellant burns. In this case, the throat diameter is getting larger as the propellant burns. As the throat hole gets larger, it takes more propellant weight flow to maintain a constant chamber pressure.

All of these relationships can be summed up in one simple equation for the chamber pressure as a function of burn area, throat area, C* and burn rate equation parameters.

$$P_c = [(K_n) * (c) * (\rho) * (C*/32.2)]^{[1/(1-n)]}$$

Where:
K_n = (Propellant burning surface area)/(Throat area)
ρ = Propellant density (lbm/inch^3)

An examination of the equation shows three key points. First, for a given propellant formulation, the chamber pressure is controlled entirely by K_n or the ratio of the propellant burning surface area to throat area. As the ratio goes up, the chamber pressure goes up. If the ratio goes down, the chamber pressure goes down. Second, for a given propellant grain pattern and non-eroding throat diameter, the only way to change the chamber pressure is to change the propellant formulation so the burn rate or density are changed. Finally, if the propellant is fixed and the ratio of propellant area to throat area is fixed, the only way to change the chamber pressure is to change C*. Increasing or decreasing the combustion efficiency of the motor can do this.

Pressed Powder Propellants

Pressed powder propellant usually has the highest burn rates of all solid propellants. Typical propellants are black powder and zinc sulfur. The burn rate is mainly controlled by the density of the propellant, which comes from the amount of pressure used to compact the powders. These propellants are useful where the propellant area to throat area is small such as in small model rocket engines. The throat hole in these engines can only be so small and with a limit volume for the motor, the propellant area is severely restricted in size. To get a meaningful chamber pressure and thrust, the solution is to use a high burn rate propellant.

In the early days of amateur rocketry, the most common class of amateur propellants was packed powder consisting of black powder, zinc-sulfur or other high burn rate powders. Today, commercial model rocket engines use some variation of black. Zinc-sulfur has been known to burn from 14 to 290 inches/second. These propellants do follow the burn rate equation mentioned earlier. For pressed black powder, the values for c and n are 1.21 and 0.24 respectively, with the burn rate in mm/second and pressure in atmospheres as reported by J.A. Conkling, Chemistry of Pyrotechnics, Marcel Decker, 1985. Values for c and n using zinc/sulfur were not available, but there is some information compiled by the US Army Artillery and Missile School at Ft. Sill, Oklahoma. They were characterizing zinc/sulfur propellant because in the 1950's they believed it be a suitable amateur rocket propellant. The optimum mixture was 2.04 parts zinc to 1 part sulfur by weight, compacted to a density of 161 lbs/ft3 or a specific gravity of 2.58. At 1000 psi, the propellant properties where as follows:

- Burn rate = 90 inches/second
- Flame Temperature = 2600 F
- Effective Exhaust Velocity = 1490 ft/second
- Specific Heat Ratio = 1.25
- Molecular Weight = 97.45 lbs per mole
- Specific Impulse = 45 seconds

Pressed powder propellants are commonly produced by companies for model rocket engines. When produced by professional equipment these motors are very reliable and safe. This equipment overcomes the major problem with pressed powders such as a consistent density from motor to motor and no cracks in the propellant. However, pressed powder rocket motors are dangerous for the amateur to produce since the propellant can easily be ignited by a spark. Before the propellant powder is pressed into the motor, it is loose with a fairly low density. In this form if accidentally ignited, it will burn so fast that is almost consumed instantaneously. If anyone is in the vicinity, severe burns can result.

<u>Potassium Nitrate and Sugar Propellants</u>

The amateur rocketry propellant used by my high school rocket club in the 1960`s was a mixture of sugar and potassium nitrate, sometimes referred to as "Carmel Candy" propellant. This mixture was melted in a pot and poured molten into rocket chambers where it would harden like a brick. Our rockets were almost certain to explode 90% of the time, but that was almost as exciting to watch as the few that worked perfectly and soared out of sight.

A major problem with "Carmel Candy" is that they are too brittle. The brittleness of this propellant can cause them to crack due to sudden ignition pressure, from flight loads or from pressure oscillations inside the motor chamber. Once these grains crack, there is a sudden increase in burning surface area. This increased burning surface area leads to excessive chamber pressure and an explosion

This propellant has seen renewed interest by amateurs with sucrose, dextrose and sorbitol substituted for common table sugar. Table 3-1 shows some of the properties of these classes of potassium nitrate propellants. Amateurs are experimenting with different variations of this class of propellant to get it more flexible with some limited success. However, in my opinion, the best, most reliable propellant for the amateur is composite propellant.

Generic Potassium Nitrate/Sugar Propellants
65% Potassium Nitrate by Weight -Balance is Fuel
Table 3-1

Properties	Sucrose	Dextrose	Sorbitol
Density (lb/inch^3)	0.0683	0.0678	0.0657
C* (ft/second)	3106	2993	3076
Burn rate @ 1000 psia (inch/sec.)	0.602	0.509	0.443
Burn rate coefficient, c	0.0665	(a)	(a)
Burn rate exponent, n	0.32	(a)	(a)

(a) - Burn rate behavior does not follow standard burn rate equation.

<u>Composite Propellants</u>

In a composite propellant, the fuel and oxidizer particles are suspended in a binder that has

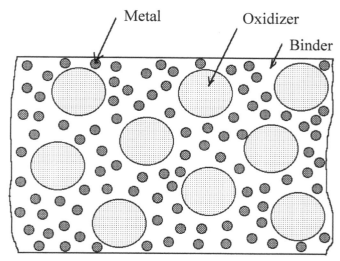

Metal   Oxidizer

Binder

Figure 3-2: Composite Solid Propellant Schematic

the physical properties of a rubber, Figure 3-2. The first thing this does is eliminate brittleness. Composite propellant is so flexible that it can bend without cracking like large erasers. This flexibility eliminates propellant cracking during ignition, handling and flight loads that enhances reliability.

The second benefit of composite propellants is the possibility of using a variety of different oxidizers and fuels in endless combinations. This leads to higher performance solid rocket propellants with the addition of metal powders. The most common metals used in all large solid rocket motors are aluminum or magnesium powder.

Composite Propellant Fuels

From our high school chemistry, remember those days of fun and joy, we know that combustion can only take place in the presence of a fuel and oxidizer. In solid rocket propellants, there are a variety of fuels:

- Aluminum
- Magnesium
- Beryllium
- Boron

Sometimes, the binder in the propellant is used as the main fuel. Any chemical that will react with the oxidizer used in the propellant can serve as the fuel. In typical Space booster rocket motors, the binder and a metal powder serve as the fuel.

Composite Propellant Oxidizers

The oxidizer in solid rocket motors is the chemical that provides oxygen for the combustion process. Typical oxidizers are ammonium perchlorate, ammonium nitrate and potassium nitrate. Their chemical composition, density and the amount of oxygen available as a function of weight percentage are listed in Table 3-2.

Composite Propellant Oxidizers
Table 3-2

Oxidizer	Composition	Density	Wt % O2 Available (%)
Ammonium Perchlorate	NH_4ClO_4	0.070	34.0
Ammonium Nitrate	NH_4NO_3	0.061	20.0
Potassium Nitrate	KNO_3	0.076	39.5
Potassium Perchlorate	$KClO_4$	0.092	46.0

Composite Propellant Binders

The binder is the key to a good composite propellant. It must hold the dry fuel and oxidizer powders together and have sufficient rubber like properties so that it will not crack under motor operating conditions. Each binder has different elastomeric properties and release different amounts of energy when burned. Typical binders are:

- PS: Polysulfide
- PVC: Polyvinyl Chloride (Yes, the same stuff in sprinkler pipes)
- PU: Polyurethane
- PBAN: Polybutadiene acrylic acid acrylonitrile terpolymer
- CTPB: Carboxyl Terminated Polybutadiene
- HTPB: Hydroxyl Terminated Polybutadiene

A popular binder for Space booster and upper stage propellants is HTPB. Professional motors typically use R45M type HTPB binder. The commercial version of this product is R45HT-LO. It is very suitable for amateur rockets and usually can be purchased cheaper than R45M. A newer binder in the HTPB class is R20LM. It has about half the viscosity of R45M or R45HT-LO, so it makes a propellant that is much easier to mix, as it is not as thick. Since R20LM binder makes an easier to mix propellant, I recommend that amateurs use this binder, even though it is a bit more expensive than R45 binders.

Plasticizers

Plasticizers are usually added to the propellant to thin it out so that it is easier to mix. It is a thin fluid, which dissolves into the binder and in some cases adds energy to the burning of the propellant. Some typical binders are:

- DOA - Dioctyl adipate
- 2-Ethylhexyle Acrylate

Composite Propellant Curing Agents

The remaining ingredient in the propellant is the curing agent. When added to the binder, it turns the liquid binder into a rubbery compound. This can take from an hour to a day or two, depending on the curing agent and the temperature of the binder while it is curing. Mondur MR is a fast acting curing agent that will cure a propellant within a few hours. It makes a very satisfactory propellant. One fast acting curing agent to avoid with ammonium nitrate propellants is 143L. While this curing agent may work satisfactory with ammonium perchlorate propellants, it produces an ammonium nitrate propellant that burns with a chuffing action.

The amount of curing agent added to the propellant controls the brittleness of the propellant. If no curing agent is added, the mixture of binder, oxidizer and fuel remains a gooey, thick mixture. If too much curing agent is added, the binder, oxidizer and fuel will form a hard, brittle propellant. The reason this occurs is due to the linking chains in the molecules of the binder. The tiny particles of solid oxidizer and solid fuel are suspended in the liquid binder. T he molecules of binder look like long chains with dangling ends. Imagine your hand as a binder molecule with your fingers representing linking chains from that molecule. Just as you can put your hands together and link your fingers together, the binder molecules can be joined together by linking the dangling chains on each molecule. If you only link one of your fingers on each hand together, you can still move your hands fairly freely. They are still very flexible. But, if you link all your fingers together, your two hands become very rigid.

If your hand were actually a binder molecule, the amount of curing agent would determine how many of your fingers would be linked together. The curing agent determines the number of dangling chains ("fingers") on each binder molecule that will be linked together. Thus, if you put in too much curing agent all the molecules of binder will be rigidly linked together and your propellant will be too brittle for use. In Chapter 4, we will give you a simple formula for calculating the exact amount of curing agent to add to your propellant.

General Composite Propellant Formulations

Composite propellants are typically organized or referenced by their binder and/or oxidizer. The amount of binder, oxidizer, fuel and curing agent are added to create in the propellant a desired performance, burn rate, strength and ease of mixing. As a general rule, ammonium perchlorate propellants will give a higher burn rate and higher specific impulse than ammonium nitrate.   The downside of ammonium perchlorate propellants is that they burn at higher temperatures and consequently are harder on nozzles and thermal insulation materials. Ammonium nitrate propellants burn slower and at lower combustion temperatures than ammonium perchlorate propellants so they give longer burn motors and are fairly easy on nozzles and insulation.   Their downside is that they have a lower specific impulse and are thicker when mixing.

Typical Ammonium Perchlorate Propellant
Table 3-3

Composition:

Ammonium perchlorate (%)	68.0
Aluminum (%)	18.0
R45M Binder(%)	14.0
Density (lb/in^3)	0.0635
Burn rate @ 1000 psia (In/sec.)	0.276
Burn rate exponent	0.40
Burn rate coefficient	0.0174
Theoretical C* (ft/second)	5200.

A Typical Ammonium Nitrate Propellant
Table 3-4

Composition:

Ammonium nitrate(%)	60.0
Magnesium (%)	20.0
R20LM Binder(%)	20.0
Density (lb/in^3)	0.0527
Burn rate @ 1000 psia (In/sec.)	0.265
Burn rate exponent	0.60
Burn rate coefficient	0.0042
Theoretical C* (ft/second)	4688.

A Recommended Starting Amateur Propellant

Solid rocket manufacturers commonly use ammonium perchlorate as the oxidizer.   It burns well with a variety of binders and metals. However, it can be hazardous to use in the production of rocket motors. Ammonium perchlorate is shock sensitive and can make clothing and other flammables auto-ignite under certain conditions. While many beginning amateurs start off making ammonium perchlorate composite propellants, I do not recommend it. In my opinion, a safer oxidizer for beginning amateurs is ammonium nitrate. It will yield a high performance propellant that is safe to produce. It is not shock sensitive and you can get it in your clothing without auto-ignition concerns.

Consequently, the propellant we recommend you start with is ammonium nitrate, magnesium, R20LM binder and MONDUR MR curing agent. This propellant was developed for use in solid rocket Space booster applications. Ammonium nitrate propellants have not been used until 1990`s, because common technical grade ammonium nitrate was unsuitable for use in industrial rocket propellants that experienced temperature cycling. The problem is that as ammonium nitrate particles go from hot to cold, the particles expand when hot, but do not contract when going back to cold. They keep getting bigger and bigger with every temperature cycle. Technical grade ammonium nitrate is not phase stabilized.

In the late 1980's, Dr. Adolf Oberth developed a low cost, non-toxic ammonium nitrate that was phase stabilized with zinc oxide. The particles would not keep growing as they were cycled from cold to hot. He also solved the second problem with ammonium nitrate propellants. They did not burn well, especially with aluminum powder fuels in the propellant. The solution was to substitute magnesium for aluminum. This new propellant ignites easily and burns very well. The reason is simple. During the combustion process, the ammonium nitrate becomes molten at 333o F. At this temperature, the magnesium reacts violently with the molten ammonium nitrate and releases great amounts of energy.

Clean up of equipment and tools contaminated with ammonium nitrate is done by simply washing them with water. The water/ammonium nitrate mixture is not hazardous waste water, but simply fertilizer ready to go on your lawn. Another benefit is that ammonium nitrate propellants have no chlorine so your solid rocket motor will not coat your launch rods or equipment with corrosive hydrochloric acid.

Technical Grade Ammonium Nitrate

While technical grade ammonium nitrate is unsuitable for industrial solid rocket motors, amateurs can use it in their propellants. Technical grade ammonium nitrate usually comes in BB sized prills that have to be ground into a powder. A chopping blade grinder works best for grinding it up. Coffee bean grinders and blenders often use this type of chopping action. The down side of using technical grade ammonium nitrate is the lack of phase stabilization. However, if you keep your propellant above freezing and below 115° F, your propellant will be ok.

Fertilizer Grade Ammonium Nitrate

Fertilizer grade ammonium nitrate is very cheap to buy, usually around five cents per pound. The problem with it is that it has a high water content that will interfere with the curing of the propellant. It also will contain other ingredients for fertilizer applications. We do not recommend using this type of ammonium nitrate.

PSAN-I Ammonium Nitrate

PSAN-I ammonium nitrate sells for about the same price as ammonium perchlorate. It is technical grade ammonium nitrate that is phase stabilized with 3% zinc oxide that is dissolved into molten ammonium nitrate. Dr. Oberth patented the process in the early 1990`s. The major advantages of using PSAN-I ammonium nitrate in your propellant is that you do not have to grind it as it is ready to use out of the bottle and you do not have to worry about the storage temperature of your finished propellant.

Formulating A Composite Propellant
Chapter 4

Many amateurs get hung up on formulating a new propellant for each motor. While industry often formulates a new propellant for each motor they make, this is not necessary for amateur rockets. A single propellant formulation that has been well characterized with respect to burn rate, performance and density can be used in a variety of different motor designs. I recommend that you formulate and characterize one or two propellants and then use those propellants in different motors. The reason is that characterizing a propellant for burn rate and performance is time consuming and requires lots of testing.

The procedures for formulating a composite propellant are basically the same for ammonium perchlorate, ammonium nitrate or any other composite propellant. We are going to look at the most common types of composite propellants. The first is an ammonium perchlorate propellant containing aluminum powder. The second is an ammonium nitrate propellant containing magnesium powder. R45HT-LO binder will be used with ammonium perchlorate and R20LM binder will be used with ammonium nitrate. Mondur MR curing agent will be used in both propellants. Although we are going to use these ingredients in the examples, you can substitute other binders and curing agents.

The first question in the formulation process is, how much of each ingredient do you put into the propellant? The answer to that depends on whether you are trying to formulate the propellant for specific impulse, flame temperature, burn rate, propellant viscosity or any combination of these or some other parameter. Its up to you, the rocket motor designer, as to what is important for your purpose. Often what yields a good propellant for one parameter works against another. So, you will have to do tradeoffs and settle on what is best for your purpose.

Ammonium Perchlorate Propellant Formulation Based on Specific Impulse

This would be important to the amateur who is trying to pack the highest impulse into a limited volume motor or wants to keep propellant weight to a minimum for a given impulse. The first question would whether to go with ammonium perchlorate or ammonium nitrate based propellant. If you are seeking maximum specific impulse with a high burn rate propellant, then your choice would be ammonium perchlorate. If you are seeking maximum specific impulse with cooler combustion temperatures or slower burn rate, than your choice would be ammonium nitrate.

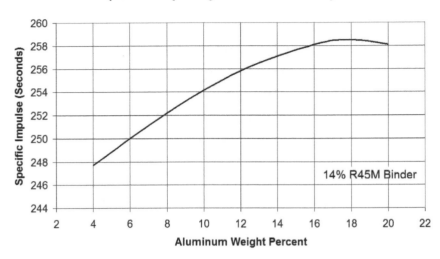

Figure 4-1: Influence of Aluminum Powder (By Weight) on the Specific Impulse of Ammonium Perchlorate Composite Propellants.

For ammonium perchlorate propellants, the general guideline would be that the more aluminum powder added, the higher the specific impulse. As a practical matter, 18% aluminum powder would be about the upper limit, Figure 4-1. As you can see from the figure after 18%, you do not get any further increase in specific impulse. With respect to binder, you want to use around 12% to 14%. As you increase the binder content, the specific impulse goes down, Figure 4-2.

Lets take an example and show how you may come up with a specific formulation based on maximizing specific impulse. First, you would decide on how "dry" you want the propellant mix. As the ammonium perchlorate and aluminum are powders, the only liquids are the binder and curing agent. As the amount of curing agent is small, it is the amount of binder that really governs how dry the mix will be. The dryer the propellant mix, the harder it will be to mix. This is analogous to mixing concrete. If you don`t have much water

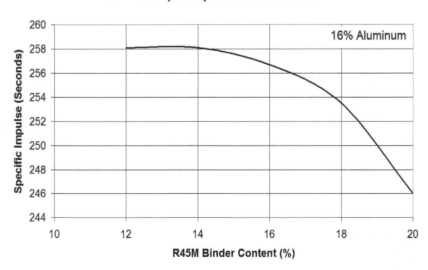

Figure 4-2: Influence of Binder Content on the Specific Impulse of Ammonium Perchlorate Propellants

in the powders, it is almost impossible to mix and get all the powders coated.

As a practical matter, about 12% is about as low as you can go without getting a fairly thick propellant that will be hard to mix. I think most amateurs would select something in the range of 16% R45M binder content. If you try this and it is too thick for you, then you can increase the binder amount to "thin" it out. You can also add plasticizers, which we will talk about later. For now, let`s say we select 16% R45M binder as the amount we will use in our propellant. You would run CHEM for different amounts of aluminum powder varying from 14% to say 20% and see where the maximum specific impulse occurred. When you run CHEM, remember that the amount of the three ingredients must add up to 100%. So for 16% R45M binder and say 18% aluminum, the amount of ammonium perchlorate would be 66%, Table 4-1.

Ammonium Perchlorate Propellant
Table 4-1

Ingredient	Weight Percentage
R45M binder	16
Aluminum	18
Ammonium Perchlorate	66
Total	100

As a standard for comparison, the chamber pressure in CHEM is set to 1000 psia and the exit pressure is set to sea level or 14.7 psia. For formulating the propellant, it does not matter that the actual motor you make will not be run at this chamber pressure. If you run all your CHEM cases at these pressure settings, then you will be able to compare all your propellant formulations on a one to one basis and see which is the best one for your purpose. At these pressures and the above propellant composition, the specific impulse would be 257 seconds. The combustion temperature would be 5338° F.

Ammonium Nitrate Propellant Formulation Based on Specific Impulse

These propellants follow the same trends as ammonium perchlorate propellants except ammonium nitrate propellants use magnesium powder instead of aluminum powder. The more magnesium the higher the specific impulse and the more binder, the lower the specific impulse, Figures 4-3 and 4-4. There are a couple of significant differences, the specific impulse peaks with a magnesium content of about 25% which is much higher than the aluminum content in ammonium perchlorate propellants. Also, the specific impulse peaks with a binder content of 12% rather than 14% for ammonium perchlorate.

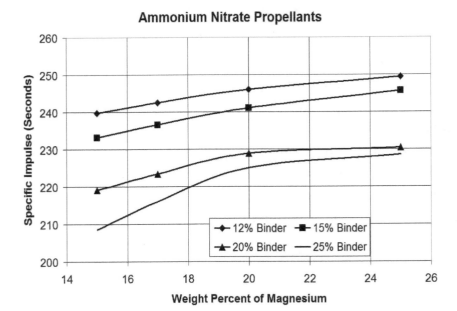

Figure 4-3: Influence of Magnesium on the Specific Impulse of Ammonium Nitrate Propellants with R45 Binder

As with ammonium perchlorate propellants, you will want to select binder content first and then select the other ingredient amounts to maximize the specific impulse. Due to the lower density of ammonium nitrate compared to ammonium perchlorate, ammonium nitrate propellants will be a lot thicker than ammonium perchlorate propellants for the same amount of binder. A 14% binder content is probably the lower limit for ammonium nitrate propellants. A binder content of 20% is actually a more practical binder content for ammonium nitrate propellants. For maximum specific impulse we would pick a magnesium content of 25% and the ammonium nitrate content would be 55% so all the ingredients would add up to 100%, Table 4-2. Using a chamber pressure of 1000 psia and exit pressure of 14.7 psia, the specific impulse would be 230 seconds and the combustion temperature would be 3755° F based on CHEM.

Ammonium Nitrate Propellant
Table 4-2

Ingredient	Weight %
R45M binder	20
Magnesium	25
Ammonium Nitrate	55
Total	100

Comparing this to the ammonium perchlorate propellant

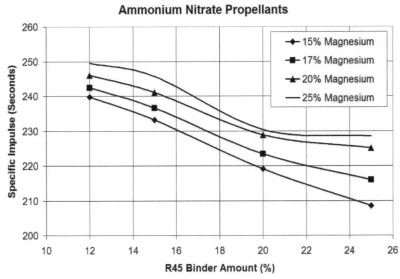

Figure 4-4: Influence of Binder on the Specific Impulse of Ammonium Nitrate Propellants

results, we see that the ammonium nitrate specific impulse is about 27 seconds lower. The combustion temperature of the ammonium nitrate is 1583 degrees cooler than ammonium perchlorate. We can put these results into better perspective by comparing the weight of propellant required to achieve the same thrust level for a fixed burn time between the two propellants just formulated. Comparing their two specific impulses can do this.

Additional amount of ammonium nitrate propellant = 257 seconds/ 230 seconds = 1.117

So, for each pound of ammonium perchlorate propellant required to produce one pound of thrust, it will take 1.117 pounds of the ammonium nitrate propellant. For small motors, this is not much of a difference. For a 100 lbs propellant ammonium perchlorate motor, the ammonium nitrate motor would need 111.7 lbs or 11.7 additional pounds of propellant. The results show that the difference for typical amateur rockets is not very significant.

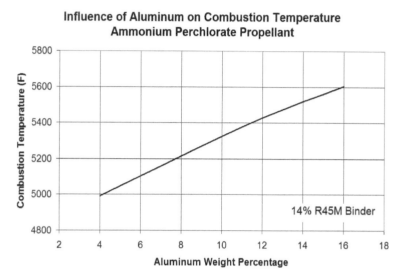

Figure 4-5: Influence of Aluminum on the Combustion Temperature of Ammonium Perchlorate Propellants at 1000 psi

Combustion temperature can often be a more important formulation parameter than specific impulse for the amateur. As just shown, the differences in propellant weights for small motors are almost insignificant. The influence of combustion temperature on the survival of motor insulation and more importantly, the nozzle is very significant. This will be discussed in more detail in Chapter 8, but nozzle materials that experience no or very little nozzle ablation with ammonium nitrate propellants, experience tremendous ablation with ammonium perchlorate propellants. For this reason, you may want to formulate based more on propellant temperature than specific impulse.

Ammonium Perchlorate Propellant Formulation Based on Combustion Temperature

To lower the combustion temperature of ammonium perchlorate propellants, you can reduce the amount of aluminum, Figure 4-5. To avoid problems with combustion stability, the amount

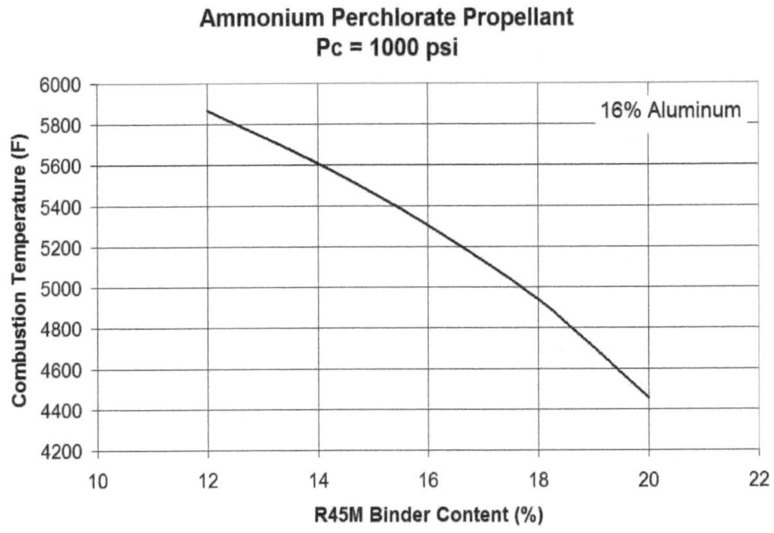

Ammonium Perchlorate Propellant
Pc = 1000 psi

Figure 4-6: Influence of Binder on the Combustion Temperature of Ammonium Perchlorate Propellants

of aluminum should not be reduced below four percent. Using our previous formulation, we will drop the aluminum content down to four percent while keeping the amount of binder the same. The combustion temperature is reduced to 4674° F and the specific impulse is now 245 seconds.

Increasing the amount of binder, Figure 4-6, can also reduce the combustion temperature. Let`s increase the binder amount from 16% to 20% while keeping the aluminum content at four percent. In this case, the combustion temperature is 3953° F while the specific impulse is further reduced to 235 seconds. This temperature and specific impulse is fairly close to the results for the ammonium nitrate propellant. However, this about the lower limit for ammonium perchlorate propellants while the combustion temperature for ammonium nitrate propellants can go even lower.

Ammonium Nitrate Propellant Formulations Based on Combustion Temperature

While the ammonium nitrate propellant formulated previously has a fairly low combustion temperature, it can be reduced even further by reducing the magnesium content, Figure 4-7. The minimum level for reducing the magnesium level and still achieving steady combustion is about 12%. If we change our previous ammonium nitrate propellant to 12 % magnesium while keeping the binder level at 20%, the combustion temperature is 2809° F and the specific impulse is reduced to 212 seconds.

As with ammonium perchlorate propellants, increasing the binder amount, Figure 4-8, can reduce the combustion temperature. As a practical matter, the most binder you want to add is probably around 22%. If we keep the magnesium level at 12% and increase the binder to 22%, the combustion temperature is 2540° F and the specific impulse is 205 seconds.

Ammonium Nitrate Propellant
Pc = 1000 psi

Figure 4-7: Influence of Magnesium on the Combustion Temperature for Ammonium Nitrate Propellants

Formulating Based on Propellant Viscosity

As mentioned earlier, the lower the amount of binder, the thicker the propellant will be after mixing. This brings us to the formulation based on mix viscosity or "Performance isn't everything". The ability to easily work with the propellant is important especially if you are going to be casting a long and skinny motor. Increasing the amount of binder or adding a plasticizer, will make the propellant more fluid and easier to work with. What propellant thickness or viscosity is right amount for you will depend on personal preference and the propellant grain pattern you are trying to cast. A long, skinny propellant pattern will generate many fine cuss words if you are trying to cast it with a thick, non-pourable propellant. A propellant grain pattern that is fat and not too long can be made with a propellant, which is as thick as, putty. The only way to get a feel for this is by mixing sample batches and casting a few motors. Again, what is acceptable to one may be intolerable to another.

Using Plasticizers

Of course, you can thin out the propellant by increasing the binder amount. But, you may not want to do that, as that would lower the performance. Another way is to use a plasticizer. Suppose we have an ammonium

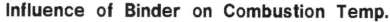

Influence of Binder on Combustion Temp.

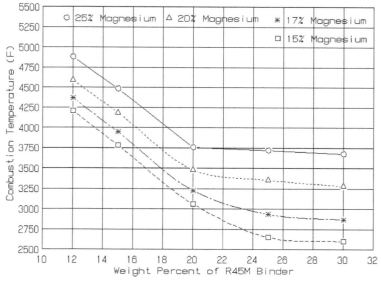

Figure 4-8: Influence of Binder Content on the Combustion Temperature for Ammonium Nitrate

nitrate propellant with 20% binder and it just too thick. We can swap out some of that 20% binder for a plasticizer. For example, we could divide up the 20% such that the binder is 15% and the plasticizer is 5%.

Binder = 15%
Plasticizer = 5%
Total = 20%

Actually you can pick whatever amount of plasticizer thins it out enough for you. Usually, the maximum amount of plasticizer is about a fourth the amount of binder. Adding more plasticizer does not thin out the binder much more and will significantly weaken the propellant after it cures. Two typical plasticizers for R45 binders are DOA and 2-Ethylhexyl Acrylate.

Oxidizer and metal particle size/shapes

An important thing to note here is that propellant formulation based on propellant viscosity is not only influenced by plasticizers and amounts of binder, but by the particle size and shapes of the powders. Typically, round particles yield a propellant with lower viscosity than powders that are ground. These round particles are usually referred to as prills or an atomized product. Visualize many tiny ball bearings flowing in a sea of binder versus many tiny plates colliding and locking in a sea of binder. The tiny ball bearings will flow freely making a freer flowing mix than plates locking up.

The right distribution of particle sizes can also help thin out the propellant without changing the amounts of the individual ingredients. You can make the oxidizer a blend of two or three different particle sizes while the metal powder can be one size. Usually, the metal powder is the smallest particle size ranging from 20 microns to 5 microns in diameter. The oxidizer may be in a blend of 200 micron and 90 micron in diameter. If the propellant uses two different particle sizes, it is called a bimodal blend. If it uses three different particle sizes, it is called a trimodal blend. A rule of thumb on selecting particle sizes is that the largest particle size is ten times larger in diameter than the smallest particle size. Usually, the particle shape has the greatest influence on reducing propellant viscosity, while the blend of particle sizes has the least.

Formulation To Increase The Propellant Burn rate

While the particle size distribution can change the thickness of the propellant, it can also increase or decrease the propellant's burn rate. Typically, small particles will increase the burn rate while larger ones will slow it down. To some extent flat, non-spherical particles will also burn faster and increase the burn rate. With ammonium perchlorate propellants, changing the ammonium perchlorate particles sizes, Table 4-3, can control the burn rate.

Influence of Particle Size on Ammonium Perchlorate Propellants
Table 4-3

Particle Size (Microns)	Burn Rate Range (Inch/second)
Coarse (400)	0.1 to 0.25
Between 400 and 6	0.25 to 1.3
6 to 2	1.3 to 2.2

For ammonium nitrate propellants, reducing the size of the magnesium powder particles has more of an influence on burn rate than the size of the ammonium nitrate particles. Magnesium particles over 200 microns slow the burn rate to the point where the propellant will hardly burn. With 20 micron magnesium particles, the propellant will ignite easily and burn at rates up to 0.3 inches per second at 1000 psi.

Besides the particle size of the ingredients, additional chemicals can be added to increase the burn rate. Some of the chemicals are listed below.

- Ammonium dichromate
- Copper oxide
- Iron oxide

Table 4-4 shows the influence of copper oxide on the burn for ammonium perchlorate propellants. These same chemicals work for ammonium nitrates, but ammonium dichromate is one of the better ones.

Influence of Copper Oxide on Ammonium Perchlorate Burn Rates
Table 4-4

Weight Percent	Burn Rate (Inch/second)	Burn Rate Exponent, n
0.5	0.74	0.53
1.0	0.84	0.30
2.0	1.04	0.31

Amount of Curing Agent

Up to now we neglected the amount of curing agent in our calculations and formulations. It has not been included in the weight percentages in the previous sections, because the amount added to the propellant is small and is not a major influence on performance or other formulating parameters. As mentioned in Chapter 3, the amount of curing agent is critical to determining whether you will end up with a good batch of propellant properly cured, a hard brittle brick or uncured goo.

The amount of curing agent will be dependent on the curing agent and the amount of binder in the propellant. The important parameter for curing agents is the curing ratio. This is the amount of curing agent weight to binder weight. This number can be calculated, but is often adjusted slightly to get the desired flexibility in the propellant. As you will recall from the previous chapter, we do not want to link all the binder. That will make it too hard and brittle.

The first guess on the curing ratio is to calculate the fully linked value and then take 80% of that number. To determine the curing ratio for full linkage, the equivalent weight of the curing agent is divided by the equivalent weight of the binder.

Curing ratio = 80% * (Equivalent weight of curing agent) / (Equivalent weight of binder)

The supplier of the binder and curing agent usually provides the equivalent weight of the binder and curing agent. The equivalent weights are shown for common binders and curing agents in Table 4-5.

Equivalent Weights/OH Ratios for Binders and Curing Agents
Table 4-5

Material	Equivalent Weight	OH Ratio	Mol. Wt.
R45HT-LO	1176	0.85	2700
R45M	1388	0.72	2600
R20LM	555	1.80	1230
Mondur MR (Curing Agent)	133	--	350
Desmodur N-3200	183	--	500

Suppose we have selected R20LM binder and Mondur MR for our propellant and want to determine the curing agent ratio. From the table we see that the equivalent weight for R20LM is 555 and the equivalent weight for Mondur MR is 133. So the curing agent ratio would be:

Curing ratio = 80% * (Mondur MR Equiv. Wt.)/(R20LM Equiv. Wt.)

Curing ratio = 0.80 * (133)/(555) = 0.80 * 0.24 = 0.19

So our first guess for a curing agent ratio using Mondur MR and R20LM binder would be 0.19. Having made this propellant, I can tell you this ratio makes a very nice flexible propellant.

Let's suppose your propellant uses R45M instead of R20LM with the Mondur MR curing agent, then the curing ratio would be:

Curing Ratio = 0.80 * (Mondur MR Equiv. Wt.)/(R45M Equiv. Wt.)

Curing Ratio = 0.80 * (133/1388) = 0.80 * 0.096 = 0.08

In this case, the amount of curing agent would be reduced due to the higher equivalent weight of R45M binder. As these calculations demonstrate, it is important to know the equivalent weight of your binder and curing agent. Unfortunately, they do vary somewhat from lot to lot of chemicals, although there are not major changes.

Using the OH Ratio and Functionality to Determine the Equivalent Weight

Many times for R45 binder the equivalent weight is listed on the bottle by the OH ratio. If you divide the OH ratio into 1000, you will obtain the equivalent weight. For example, if the OH ratio of R45HT binder is 0.85, divide that into 1000 to obtain the equivalent weight of 1176 (1000/0.85 = 1176).

If the equivalent weight is not given, it can be determined from the molecular weight and functionality. In this case, divide the molecular weight by the functionality to obtain the equivalent weight. For example, if your sample of R45M has a functionality of 2.1 and a molecular weight of 2600, then the equivalent weight would be 2600 divided by 2.1 to yield an equivalent weight of 1238 (2600/2.1 = 1238.).

You must use caution in determining the equivalent weight based on functionality and molecular weight. This method works fairly well for low molecular weight materials, but can be significantly in error for high molecular weight materials. Errors of up to 20% have been reported in the literature. So beware and always make small sample batches before making a motor when using a new curing agent and binder system.

Converting Propellant Ingredients Weight Percentage to Weights for Mixing

After you have decided on a propellant formulation with all its weight percentages, you will need to convert that to weights you can set on a balance. As an example, suppose we have decided on weight percentages of each propellant ingredient as 20% magnesium, 20% R20LM binder and 60% ammonium nitrate using the Mondur MR curing agent. We want to know now what are the weight amounts for a motor that has 2 lbs of propellant. At this point, it would be good to convert our pounds into grams since laboratory balances are calibrated in grams. As we shall see in Chapter 12, a laboratory balance will be necessary to mix the propellant.

To convert pounds into grams, simply multiply the number of pounds by 1000 and then divide by 2.2. In our case, we multiply 2 lbs by 1000 and divide by 2.2 to yield 909.1 grams (2 lbs * 1000/2.2 = 909.1). We can round this off to a whole number of 909 grams.

The total propellant batch for the motor is going to be 909 grams of propellant. To determine how many grams of each ingredient will be used in the propellant mix, we multiply the total amount of propellant by the weight percentage for each ingredient divided by 100. The weight percentages for our propellant, we determined to be 20% binder, 20% magnesium and 60% ammonium nitrate.

Amount of R20LM binder = (909 grams) * (20/100) = 181.8 grams

Amount of magnesium = (909 grams) * (20/100) = 181.8 grams

Amount of ammonium nitrate = (909 grams) * (60/100) = 545.4 grams

If the total amount of each ingredient is added together (181.8 grams + 181.8 grams + 545.4 grams), it will equal the desired total amount of propellant, which is 909 grams. It is always a good idea to add all three numbers together as a check on your calculations.

The last weight to calculate is the weight of the curing agent. We will use a curing ratio of 0.19 for the Mondur MR curing agent and R20LM binder. Referring to our propellant formulation consisting of 545.4 grams ammonium nitrate, 181.8 grams magnesium and 181.8 grams R20LM binder, we want to know how much Mondur curing agent to add to the propellant mixture. The amount of curing agent is the ratio 0.19 multiplied by the amount of binder, 181.8

grams which is to equal 34.5 grams.

$$\text{Amount of Mondur MR curing agent} = 0.19 * 181.8 \text{ grams} = 34.5 \text{ grams}$$

If you are using a plasticizer with the binder, you do not include the weight of the plasticizer. For example, if the plasticizer weight is 54 grams and the R20LM binder weight is 127.8 grams, you would multiple 0.19 by 127.8 grams to get 24.3 grams of curing agent. You do not include the 54 grams in the calculation.

At this point, we have all our weights for our propellant: R20LM = 181.8 grams, magnesium = 181.8 grams, ammonium nitrate = 545.4 grams, and Mondur MR = 34.5 grams. You will notice if we add all the weights together we now get a total propellant weight of 943.5 grams. This is a little more propellant than out target weight. While we could have gone through and calculated it exactly, it would have been a bit more complicated math, which I did not want to throw at you. Actually, I always make a little extra propellant as it can be used for igniters and test purposes.

Sample Propellant Batches

It is important to note that up to this point, all our numbers are theoretical. As mentioned earlier, many things can influence the propellant cure, flexibility and burn rate. You should always make small 50 gram test batches before you try these formulations in your rocket motor. Cast the propellant into small paper or plastic cups. After the propellant has cured, peel off the cup and slice the propellant in thin pieces with a sharp knife. It should cut fairly easily. Bend the slices to test their flexibility. They should be fairly flexible like a pencil eraser. If the propellant is tacky or still moldable, increase the amount of curing agent slightly and try again. If the propellant seems too hard or brittle, slightly decrease the amount of curing agent. As you look at your sample propellant, look for small voids or bubbles. They should be very small. If you have large frequent bubbles in the propellant, then you are not working the propellant enough in the casting process to remove the trapped air.

Another important reason for mixing sample batches is to see if the mixture is too thick or too dry to be cast into the motor. If so, you may have to use a higher binder percentage, use a plasticizer or use more of the plasticizer to thin it out. As you can see this is a back and forth process until you find a propellant formulation that suits you. A discussion on how to cast the propellant is in Chapter 13. The test batches can be disposed of by lighting one end of the sample. They will burn brilliantly with an intense white light. Direct viewing of the burning propellant should be minimized without protective tinted glasses.

Finally, you will need to know the density of your cured propellant fairly accurately to predict the motor chamber pressure. You can determine this by cutting a cylinder to a certain length. For example, suppose we have a phenolic tube that has an inside diameter of 0.88 inches and we cut off a piece that is 1 inch long. The inside volume of the phenolic cylinder is:

$$\text{Volume} = (3.14/4) * (\text{Cylinder Length}) * (\text{Inside Diameter})^2$$

$$\text{Volume} = (3.14/4) * 1.0 * (0.88)^2 = 0.785 * 1.0 * 0.7744 = 0.6079 \text{ inches}^3$$

To determine the density of your propellant, weigh the cylinder when it is empty and then when it is full of propellant. Make sure the propellant surface is flush with the edge of the cylinder. The density is:

$$\text{Density} = [(\text{Wt. of cylinder with propellant}) - (\text{Wt. of empty cylinder})]/(\text{Volume})$$

Suppose the empty weight is 16 grams and the weight loaded with propellant is 30 grams. Then the density is:

$$\text{Density} = [30 - 16]/(0.6079) = 14/0.6079 = 23.03 \text{ grams/inch}^3$$

Multiply that number by 0.0022 to convert it to lbs/inch^3:

$$\text{Density} = 23.03 \text{ grams/inch}^3 * 0.0022 = 0.0507 \text{ lbs/inch}^3$$

Preliminary Motor Design
Chapter 5

If you have been buying commercial motors, you are used to selecting a motor and then finding or designing a rocket that will work with the motor. When designing an amateur rocket, you reverse the process by first thinking of what you want the rocket to do. Then, you design a motor to make the rocket perform as desired. The difference is like buying clothes off the rack in a store or having them custom fitted to you. Off the rack, you have to make your body fit the clothes. Custom fitted, the clothes are made to fit you.

The first step in designing your motor is to determine the minimum thrust level to safely get off the launch rod or rail. You should also decide if you want a short or long duration motor. The duration of the motor will be controlled by the diameter of the motor since the bigger the diameter the longer the burn duration. The diameter of the motor is going to be controlled by the diameter of your rocket. If it is only 4 inches in diameter, you are restricted to motors with an outside diameter of less than 4 inches. Length is another consideration, but probably not a major one unless your rocket is very short. You should also consider the maximum motor weight your rocket can support before ignition of the motor. This is usually not important for the smaller diameter rockets.

The Motor Design Process

You and the limitations of your rocket determine the initial design parameters such as maximum weight, diameter, length and your flight objective. These parameters are fairly easy to determine. The remaining design parameters have to be calculated by you. The motor design process starts with selecting a thrust level and burn time. The next step is to fly your rocket with this "ideal" motor using the included trajectory computer program, FLIGHT. The trajectory program will give you the flight profile of the rocket and aerodynamic structural loads. If the flight profile is not what you want, then you can change the thrust and duration until the rocket performs as desired.

Once you have determined the desired thrust level and motor duration, it is time to design the motor ballistically to match the desired thrust-time curve as best you can. This involves the selection of a propellant geometry and formulation. After the ballistic performance of the motor has been set, the design needs to be checked both thermally and structurally. The thermal analysis will be used to verify insulation thicknesses and particularly the estimated throat erosion. The structural nozzle thicknesses plus the adequacy of the bulkhead and nozzle retaining method.

The final step is to blend back into the ballistic analysis the results of the thermal and structural analysis. For example, the calculated throat erosion will now be used in the ballistic analysis. It might also be necessary to reduce the outer diameter of the propellant, if more insulation is required in the motor.

Based on the new ballistic results, you may have to alter the propellant geometry or formulation to better match the desired thrust-time curve. You may also want to change the throat material to obtain a different throat erosion rate to better match the desired thrust-time curve. Depending on the amount of propellant geometry or formulation changes, you may have to look at the motor thermally and structurally, again.

The design process is basically a loop between the ballistic, thermal and structural analysis of the motor. How many times you have to go around the loop depends on how close your design results match your goals and how close you want them to match.

Starting the Design Process

Let's start the design process with an example that can be carried throughout Chapters 6 through 9. Our rocket is a scratch build rocket with the following general characteristics.

- Diameter: 3.25 inches
- Empty Weight (Less Motor): 6 lbs
- Estimated Drag Coefficient: 0.4

With this information, we are ready to take the first step and calculate the motor thrust to weight of the rocket ratio. This is generally referred to as the thrust to weight ratio. The minimum thrust to weight ratio must be known so that the rocket will come off the launch rod at a speed where it is aerodynamically stable. A fin-guided rocket will typically require a minimum airspeed of about 40 ft/second by the end of the launch rod or tower in order to be stable in flight.

Suppose we will be using a launch rod 7 ft long and we want to leave the rod at 40 ft/second. Using this information, we can calculate the initial required thrust to weight ratio to leave the rod at this speed. The required acceleration of the rocket off the rod is the desired velocity squared divided by the rod length:

Initial Rocket Acceleration = a_{rod} = (Rocket Velocity Off Rod)^2 / [2 * (Rod Length)]

Initial Rocket Acceleration = $(40)^2 / 14 = 1600/14 = 114.3$ ft/second^2

We can divide the initial rocket acceleration by 32.2 ft/second^2 to obtain the required acceleration in "g"s. In this case, 114.3 divided by 32.2 equals 3.55 or about 3.5 g's of acceleration. To obtain the initial thrust to weight ratio, we simply add one g to this result representing the initial weight of the rocket.

Initial Thrust to Weight Ratio = F/W = (a_{rod} in g's) + 1

Initial Thrust to Weight Ratio = F/W = (3.5) + 1 = 4.5

In order for our rocket to come off the launch rod so the rocket is stable, the initial thrust of the rocket motor must be 4.5 times the launch weight of the rocket. The launch weight is the empty weight of the rocket plus the weight of the rocket motor. If we knew the launch weight of the rocket, then we would know the required initial thrust level. Unfortunately, while we know the empty weight of the rocket, we do not know how much the rocket motor weighs. But, how do we get it or is there another way?

Well, there is another way if we take advantage of another motor parameter called propellant mass fraction. The propellant mass fraction is the weight of propellant in a motor divided by the total motor weight.

Propellant Mass Fraction = f_p = (Weight of Propellant)/(Total Motor Weight)

Propellant mass fraction can be as low as 0.50 for PVC pipe rocket motors. It can be up to 0.85 for a well designed metal case motor. In our example, we are going to make the motor out of PVC pipe, so we will pick a mass fraction of 0.50. Combining this knowledge with our previous relationship for the initial thrust relative to lift-off weight, we obtain two equations we can solve for initial thrust:

Initial Thrust = (Motor Weight + Rocket Weight) * (Acceleration off rod in g's)

Motor Weight = (Weight of Propellant)/(Propellant Mass Fraction)

I'm not going to go through the derivation so your eyes should not start to gloss over here. The bottom line is as follows:

Initial Thrust = F_i = [f_p * W_r) / [(f_p/{F/W}) - (t_b/Isp)]

5-3

Where:

f_p = Propellant mass fraction

W_r = Weight of rocket without motor (lbs)

F/W = Thrust to weight ratio

t_b = Burn time (seconds)

Isp = Specific Impulse (seconds)

We now know everything to determine the initial thrust, but the specific impulse and burn time. We can calculate the specific impulse of the propellant and motor by selecting a propellant formulation and chamber pressure as was discussed in the last chapter. Let's say we select a chamber pressure of 350 psi and for our propellant formulation we calculate a specific impulse of 206 seconds using the CHEM software. The last item to select is the burn time. Knowing the burn time, we can then calculate the initial thrust for our motor. Suppose we let the burn time be 5 seconds. Then, we can calculate the required initial thrust:

$$F_i = (0.5 * 6)/[(0.5/4.5) - (5/206)] = 3/[0.1111 - 0.0243] = 3/0.0868 = 34.5 \text{ lbs}$$

$$\text{Initial Thrust} = F_i = 34.5 \text{ lbs}$$

From the thrust to weight ratio, we can calculate the total rocket weight at lift-off by dividing the initial thrust by the thrust to weight ratio:

$$\text{Lift-off Rocket Weight} = (Fi) / (F/W) = 34.5 / 4.5 = 7.67 \text{ lbs}$$

The motor weight can be found by subtracting the rocket weight from the lift-off rocket weight:

$$\text{Motor Weight} = \text{Lift-off Rocket Weight} - \text{Rocket Weight} = 7.67 - 6.00 = 1.67 \text{ lbs}$$

We can calculate the propellant weight by multiplying the motor weight of 1.67 lbs by the propellant mass fraction of 0.5 to obtain 0.835 lbs (1.69 * 0.50 = 0.835). We can double check our calculations by using the relationship from Chapter 1 relating propellant weight flow and specific impulse to thrust. If we plug into that equation the calculated propellant weight, selected burn time and specific impulse, we should get the initial thrust.

$$F_i = (\text{Specific Impulse}) * (\text{Propellant Weight}) / (\text{Burn Time}) = 206 * 0.835 / 5.0 = 34.4 \text{ lbs}$$

When you consider round-off error in our calculations, this checks fairly well with our previously calculated value for initial thrust, F_i. It's always good to make this double check on your calculations to catch a mistake before you get into it too deep.

Finally, we want to determine our total motor impulse. Combining some of the equations in Chapter 1, we can come up with an expression for total impulse based on propellant weight and specific impulse;

$$\text{Motor Impulse} = I = (\text{Weight of Propellant}) * (\text{Specific Impulse})$$

Then for our motor:

$$\text{Motor Impulse} = I = 0.835 * 206 = 172.01 \text{ lb-seconds}$$

For those of you who relate to Newton-seconds, multiply this number by 4.445 to obtain 764.6 Newton-seconds (172.01 * 4.445 = 764.6). If you also like letter designations for your motors, you can look this up in Table 5-1. It appears that this motor falls in the "J" range.

Rocket Motor Classes by Letter Designation
Table 5-1

Class	Total Impulse Range (Newton-Second)
G	80 - 160
H	161 - 320
I	321 - 640
J	641 - 1,280
K	1,281 - 2,650
L	2,651 - 5,120
M	5,121 - 10.240
N	10,241 - 20,480
O	20,481 - 40,960
P	40,961 - 81,920
Q	81,921 - 163,840
R	163,841 - 327,680
S	327,681 - 655,360
T	655,361 - 1,310,720

We are now ready to fly our rocket with our preliminary motor using the FLIGHT trajectory software. Although we do not know the thrust-time curve for our motor yet, we can assume a constant thrust at the initial value to get an estimate of how high the rocket may go. We will also assume a sea level launch at a launch angle of one degree. It is very hard to get a launch rod truly set to zero degrees or perfectly vertical.

The result of the first flight shows that rocket achieves an altitude of 4,477 ft in about 18.0 seconds. The maximum aerodynamic compressive force on the rocket is less than eight lbs. The aerodynamic forces are certainly not excessive and will be useful in designing the rocket body tube to withstand these forces in Chapter 16.

The question now is, "Do I settle for this or do I tweak the design some more, say for more altitude or whatever?" The answer is really up to you. I think I'll stick with this preliminary design, but I could adjust it if I wanted to. The important thing is don't go on to the next step if you are not satisfied with the rocket's projected flight.

In summary, we now know our motor has the following parameters:

- Lift-off Thrust = 34.4 lbs
- Thrust Duration = 5 seconds
- Total Impulse = 172.01 Lb-sec or 764.6 N-Sec (J Class Motor)
- Motor Weight = 1.67 lbs
- Propellant Weight = 0.835 lbs

The only thing left to do is design a motor that will give us these performance and weight numbers. That brings us to the next chapter.

Rocket Motor Ballistic/Performance Analysis
Chapter 6

At this point, we are ready to design the actual motor by determining the propellant grain pattern, throat diameter, bore diameter and a motor diameter. Our design goal is to obtain a lift-off thrust of 34.4 lbs with an average duration of five seconds and a total impulse of 172.0 lb-seconds. From our CHEM runs, we calculated a C* for our propellant formulation of 4,665 ft/second. Our chamber pressure is 350 psi. The propellant weight flow is the weight of propellant divided by the burn time:

Propellant weight flow = (Propellant weight) / (Burn time) = 0.835 / 5 = 0.167 lb/second

We can calculate the throat area and throat diameter as follows:

Throat Area = [(Propellant Weight Flowrate) * C*] / [(Chamber Pressure) * 32.2]

Throat Area = [(0.167) * (4665)] / (350 * 32.2) = [779.06] / (11270.) = 0.069 in²

The throat area can be converted to a throat diameter using the following equation:

Throat Diameter = Square Root [1.274 * (Throat Area)] = Square Root [1.274 * 0.069]

Throat Diameter = Square Root (0.0879) = 0.296 inches

We now know that our initial motor throat diameter should be 0.296 inches or a little less than 5/16 inch. At this point, we can calculate the exit diameter of the exit cone. You want to make sure the exit cone will not over expand the exhaust gases to the point where the exit pressure is less than atmospheric pressure. Remember, we planned to launch at sea level where the atmospheric pressure is 14.7 psia. So, we will set the exit pressure to 14.7. Then, we can calculate the exit pressure to chamber pressure ratio.

P_e/P_c = (Exit pressure) / (Chamber pressure) = (14.7) / (350) = 0.042

We then go to Appendix H and look under P_e/P_c to find the closest value to 0.042. We see that an expansion ratio of 3.9 gives an approximate P_e/P_c value that is a little higher than 0.042. Its P_e/P_c values is estimated to be 0.0424 while the corresponding thrust coefficient is approximately 1.408. Using the P_e/P_c value for an expansion ratio of 3.9, we calculate the exit pressure as:

Exit pressure = P_e = (P_e/P_c) * (Chamber Pressure) = 0.0424 * 350 = 14.84 psia

We can now calculate the thrust of the motor based on the throat area and thrust coefficient.

Thrust = (Chamber pressure) * (Throat area) * (Thrust coefficient)

Thrust = (350) * (0.069) * (1.408) = 34.00 lbs

This is very close to what we wanted so we are still on track with our motor design. Finally, we can calculate the exit cone diameter based on the expansion ratio. Our expansion ratio is 3.9, then:

Exit diameter = d_e = (Throat diameter) * square root (Expansion ratio)

d_e = 0.296 * square root (3.9) = 0.296 * 1.9748 = 0.5845 inch

Let's summarize what we now know about the motor.

- Thrust = 34 lbs
- Throat Diameter = 0.296 inch
- Exit cone diameter = 0.5845 inch
- Chamber pressure = 350 psia
- Thrust duration = 5 seconds
- Total impulse = 172.0 lb-seconds
- Motor weight = 1.67 lbs
- Propellant weight = 0.835 lbs
- Propellant weight flow rate = 0.167 lb/second

The propellant I selected in the last chapter that gives a specific impulse of 206 seconds at a chamber pressure of 350 psia consists of 20% R20LM binder, 20% magnesium powder and 60% ammonium nitrate. CHEM estimates the density at 0.0574 lb/in³. This density is on the high side, as it does not consider voids and particle packing voids in the actual propellant. From propellant sample batches, I have measured the propellant density at 0.0527 lb/in³. This is the propellant density that will be used in our calculations.

The next parameter we need to determine is the burn rate for our propellant at a 350 psia chamber pressure. We know that the chamber pressure is defined as:

$$\text{Burn rate} = c * (P_c)^n$$

The coefficient, c, and exponent, n, are determined experimentally for a particular formulation and will vary depending on the amounts, shapes and sizes of the chemicals in the propellant. If you have a brand new formulation, the best way to determine these parameters is to conduct strand burning rate tests as explained in Appendix F. However, if you cannot afford to build and conduct such tests, you will have to make an estimate. Based on motor firings, you can then revise your estimates to get better numbers. So that you are not completely in the dark, we have listed some numbers for typical propellants in Table 6-1. Use these numbers with caution as many variables can change these numbers for your particular formulation.

Some Typical Burn Rate Parameters for
Ammonium Nitrate, Magnesium, R45HT and Mondur MR Propellants
Table 6-1

AN	Mg	Binder	Mg Particle Mesh	c	n
60%	20%	20% R45HT or M	-250 (ground)	0.0085	0.4
60%	20%	20% R45HT or M	-650 (prill)	0.0030	0.6
60%	20%	20% R20LM	-650 (prill)	0.0034	0.6

Suppose for our propellant, we have determined from experimental data that the value for c is 0.0046 and n is 0.6. Using the burning rate equation and a chamber pressure of 350 psi, the initial burn rate will be:

$$\text{Burn Rate} = 0.0046 * (350)^{0.6} = 0.0046 * 33.608 = 0.155 \text{ inches/second}$$

The next step is to calculate the initial propellant burning surface area. Recalling from Chapter 3, the propellant weight flow rate for a solid propellant is:

Propellant weight flow rate = (Propellant density) * (Propellant burn area) * (Burn rate)

This can be rewritten to solve for the propellant burn area:

Propellant burn area = (Propellant weight flow rate)/[(Propellant density)*(Burn rate)]

Propellant burn area = (0.167) / [(0.0527) * (0.155)] = 0.167 / 0.00817 = 20.44 in^2

This is the required propellant surface area to generate a chamber pressure of 350 psia for the throat diameter already calculated. All that is left is to select a propellant grain pattern that gives this surface area. There are five basic grain patterns and Table 6-2 lists the characteristics of each grain pattern with and without an eroding nozzle throat.

Propellant Grain Pattern Characteristic Relative to
Thrust-Time Curves
Table 6-2

Grain Pattern	No Throat Erosion	Throat Erosion
End Burner	Constant Thrust	Decreasing Thrust
Core Burner	Increasing and Hump Thrust	Increasing, Hump or Decreasing Thrust
Moon Burner	Increasing and Decreasing Thrust	Constant or Decreasing Thrust
C-Slot Burner	Increasing and Decreasing Thrust	Increasing and Decreasing Thrust
Segmented Burner	Increasing, Hump or Thrust	Increasing, Hump or Thrust

To make things simple, we would like a constant thrust during the burn time with a non-eroding throat. In this case, the propellant surface area must be constant with burn time. The most obvious choice would be an end burner with a constant propellant area. The propellant surface area for an end burner is calculated as follows:

End burning surface area = (3.14 / 4) * (Propellant diameter)^2

This can be rewritten as follows to get solve for the propellant diameter:

End burning propellant diameter = square root [(4) * (End burning surface area) / 3.14]

= square root [(4) * (20.44) / 3.14] = square root [81.76 / 3.14] = square root [26.04]

End burning propellant diameter = 5.10 inches

This diameter is larger than the diameter of our rocket. It could work if we redesigned our rocket to this diameter. However, we would have to recalculate altitude on this diameter and

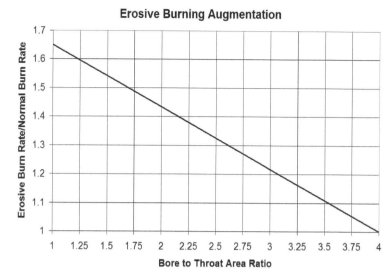

Erosive Burning Augmentation

Figure 6-1: Burnrate Augmentation Due to Erosive Burning in Ammonium Nitrate Propellants

the empty weight of the rocket would most likely go up as well. If we redesigned the rocket to a little over five inches without increasing the weight, an end burning motor could be a viable option.

A straight core or segmented grain pattern can give a "Hump" type thrust-time curve. The thrust starts and ends at the same value and rises to a higher thrust level during the middle of the burn. This could be an acceptable alternative to a constant thrust. Both a straight core and a segmented grain pattern have a bore hole down the middle. The first thing we need to do is calculate the bore diameter. In selecting a bore diameter, we want to eliminate, if possible, erosive burning of the propellant.

Erosive burning occurs when the ratio of the bore diameter to the throat diameter is less than two. When the bore to throat diameters are less than two, the propellant gases in the bore are traveling at Mach 0.15 or higher. When the gases are flowing past the burning propellant surface at this speed, it greatly increases the burning rate. The amount of erosive burning is dependent on propellant formulation and a variety of other parameters besides gas velocity in the bore. For an ammonium nitrate, magnesium and HTPB propellant, there is not any erosive burning data to use for developing erosive burning augmentation factors. However, we have estimated the amount of erosive burning based on an AP, aluminum, and HTPB propellant with a burn rate similar to ammonium nitrate propellant, Figure 6-1.

In our case, we are going to size the bore to avoid erosive burning. To do this we will set the bore diameter to two times the throat diameter. So that:

Bore diameter = 2 * (Throat diameter) = 2 * 0.296 = 0.592 inches

The burn time will be the time it takes for the propellant to burn through the propellant web, which is defined as the propellant thickness in the radial direction, Figure 6-2. Knowing the burn time and burn rate, we can calculate the propellant web thickness:

Propellant web thickness = (Burn time) * (Propellant burn rate)

Propellant web thickness = (5) * (0.155) = 0.775 inches

This can be used to calculate the propellant outer diameter.

Propellant outer diameter = [(2) * (Propellant web thickness)] + (Bore diameter)

Propellant outer diameter = [2 * 0.775] + 0.592 = 1.55 + 0.592 = 2.142 inches

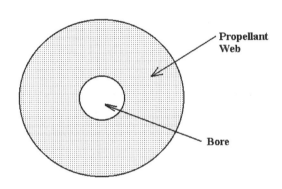

Figure 6-2: Web Thickness on a Propellant Grain

So, the outer diameter of the propellant must be 2.142 inches to get a burn time of five seconds. This would be reasonable for our three inch diameter rocket. If we were to make the motor out of PVC pipe we would have to use 2.5 inch PVC. If we wanted to make the motor out of two inch PVC pipe, we would have to make the bore smaller so we could increase the web thickness. In that case, we would be entering the erosive burning regime. That is not necessarily bad as I have designed and successfully flown many motors with the bore to throat diameter ratios down around 1.5.

As we would like to use a two inch PVC pipe for the motor if possible, lets try a ratio of 1.5 for the bore to throat diameter. Then.

Bore diameter = 1.5 * 0.296 = 0.444 inch

The web thickness stays the same so the new outer diameter would be:

Propellant outer diameter = [2 * 0.775] + 0.444 = 1.994 inches

This still is too large when we consider that we will have to insulate the two inch PVC pipe with rubber insulation. So, it looks like we will have to go with 2.5 inch PVC pipe for the chamber.

Now to get the "hump" type thrust-time curve, initial propellant surface area must be equal to the final propellant surface area.

Initial burning area = (3.14) * (Bore diameter) * (Propellant length) + ([3.14/2] * [(Outer diameter)^2 - (Bore diameter)^2])

Final burning area = (3.14) * (Outer propellant diameter) * (Burned propellant length)

Burned propellant length = (Propellant length) - [(Outer diameter) - (Bore diameter)]

If we set the initial area equal to the final area, we can solve for the initial propellant length. Don't worry I'm going to skip the derivation. Here are the results:

Initial propellant length = [Do - Db + {(Do^2 - Db^2)/(2*Do)}]/[1-(Db/Do)]

Where:

Do = Propellant outer diameter
Db = Propellant bore diameter

If our bore diameter is 0.592 inches and the propellant outer diameter is 2.142 inches, then the initial grain length is 3.51 inches with a propellant area of 13.18 square inches. You can use FPRED to do the math for you. We want a propellant area of 20.44 square inches. To get that, we would need to use a segmented grain pattern where each segment has 13.18 square inches.

Number of propellant segments = (Total propellant area) / (Segment area)

Number of propellant segments = 20.44 / 13.18 = 1.55 segments

We cannot have fractional segments, so we would have to settle for either one or two. With one we would be way under on the thrust or way over. At this point, it would probably be best to adjust the bore diameter and outer propellant diameter to dimensions that reflect the physical dimensions of the motor.

We are going to use 2.5 inch PVC pipe for the chamber and it is going to be a segmented pattern. From our previous calculations, we know that if we make the bore 0.444 inches, the outer diameter will be 1.994 inches. That is approximately the inside diameter of two inch PVC pipe. We could use two inch PVC pipe as propellant cartridges and slide those inside a

2.5 inch PVC pipe for the chamber. For a bore diameter of 0.444 inches and a propellant outer diameter of 1.994 inches, the propellant length would be 3.21 inches with a propellant area of 10.41 square inches. The number of propellant segments would be:

$$\text{Number of propellant segments} = 20.44 / 10.41 = 1.96$$

So, our motor will have two propellant segments that are 3.21 inches long with a bore diameter of 0.444 inches. The propellant will be cast into two inch PVC pipe. At this point, we need to calculate our propellant weight.

$$\text{Weight of propellant} = (\text{Number of segments}) * (\text{Propellant per segment})$$

$$\text{Propellant weight per segment} = (\text{Density}) * (3.14/4) * (\text{Segment length}) * [(\text{Outer diameter})^2 - (\text{Bore diameter})^2]$$

$$\text{Propellant weight per segment} = 0.0527 * 0.785 * 3.21 * [(1.994)^2 - (0.444)^2]$$

$$= 0.0527 * 0.785 * 3.21 * [3.976 - 0.197] = 0.0527 * 0.785 * 3.21 * 3.779$$

$$\text{Propellant weight per segment} = 0.502 \text{ lbs}$$

For two segments, that would give us a total propellant weight of one pound, which is over the desired amount. We are over on the amount of propellant. This will increase the propellant weight flow rate and consequently the chamber pressure during the midpoint of the motor burn. At this point, let's run FPRED and see how the motor performs.

When we look at the pressure-time curve we see that the mid point pressure climbs up to 670 psi which would cause the PVC pipe chamber to burst. We need to get the peak pressure down and reduce the propellant weight without reducing the initial thrust below our desired value of 34.4 lbs. This can be done a couple of ways. First, the propellant segment lengths can be reduced to three inches to reduce the propellant weight. This reduces the peak pressure to 576 psi and the propellant by only a small amount. We can also increase the bore diameter to 5/8 inches to reduce propellant weight, although this will reduce the burn time. The results for this case show the propellant weight is 0.89 lbs with a peak pressure of 657 psi. We can drop the pressure and the initial thrust closer to our goal by increasing the throat diameter to 0.32 inches. The peak pressure in this case is 444 psi with an initial thrust of 36.4 lbs and a burn time of about 4.25 seconds. This pressure is still too high for PVC pipe.

While we originally planned to use a non-eroding nozzle like graphite, a switch to an eroding nozzle like CE phenolic would open the throat hole during the motor burn and keep the maximum pressure down. In order to run FPRED, you need to know what throat erosion rate to input into FPRED. You can use the pressure-time curve from FPRED to make an initial estimate. First we have to estimate the average chamber pressure with an eroding throat. Let's make our initial guess 200 psi. So we go up from the 0.32 inches on the throat diameter axis until we hit the line representing an average chamber pressure of 200 psi. The corresponding throat erosion rate is 19 mils/second. When that value is input into FPRED we see from looking at the chamber pressure-time curve that the average pressure is about 100 psi. Going back to the pressure-time curve we can estimate that the throat erosion would be about half what we would have from a 200 psi chamber pressure.

We continue to run FPRED with different erosion rates based on average chamber pressure until the erosion rate corresponds to the calculated average pressure from FPRED. After doing that, we end up with an average chamber pressure of 120 psi corresponding to an erosion rate of 12 mils/second. This motor has a peak pressure that is acceptable along with an initial thrust that is close to our goal. At this point, we are probably close enough to our design goals to say this is the motor we will build.

Let's summarize our motor design:

- Initial thrust = 36.3 lbs
- Average thrust = 19.6 lbs
- Throat diameter = 0.32 inch
- Exit cone diameter = 0.5845 inch
- Average chamber pressure = 120 psia
- Thrust duration = 9.0 seconds
- Total impulse = 183.7 lb-seconds
- Motor weight = 1.78 lbs
- Propellant weight = 0.89 lbs
- CE Phenolic nozzle
- 2.5 inch PVC pipe chamber
- Two segments of propellant cast into 2 inch PVC pipe
- Length of propellant segment = 3.0 inches
- Bore diameter = 0.625 inches

Motor Structural Analysis
Chapter 7

The next step in the motor design process is to see if your motor is structurally sound. In other words, will it explode? Normally, if you are working with PVC pipe, fittings and end caps this is not necessary if you stay at or under the rated working pressure. In our case, we will be exceeding the working pressure by a considerable margin so we will take a look at the wall thicknesses. In general, the basic failure scenarios for rocket motors are as follows:

- Chamber Failure - Chamber wall rupture
- Nozzle Failure - Nozzle wall rupture
- Bulkhead Failure - Bulkhead wall rupture
- Nozzle and/or Bulkhead Loss - Nozzle and/or Bulkhead ejection during firing
- O-ring failure

When you are designing a new motor, each of these different failure scenarios should be examined to see if they are likely to occur during the motor firing. The cause of each failure may be from different sources.

Chamber Wall Thickness

This first type of structural failure is due to the chamber wall being too thin to contain the maximum expected operating pressure or MEOP of the motor. The output from FPRED will give the MEOP for your motor design. In our case, the MEOP is 320 psi. The chamber will be 2.5 inch diameter PVC pipe with a maximum rated working pressure of 300 psi. The minimum wall thickness is calculated using the following formula:

Min. Wall Thickness = [(MEOP) * (Chamber Diameter)]/[2 * (Ultimate Tensile Strength)]

Table 7-1 lists the allowable stress for a variety of materials. For PVC, the ultimate tensile strength is 7,450 psi. Using our formula, we can calculate the thinnest possible wall thickness for PVC pipe.

Min. Wall Thickness = [320 * 2.5]/[2 * 7450] = 800/14900 = 0.054 inches

If the wall thickness of the chamber is any amount smaller than 0.054 inch, then the chamber wall will rupture during motor operation. In reality, we would want a safety factor to account for variance in wall thickness and possible changes in chamber pressure above MEOP. For our motor, we would like a safety factor of two. Then, our chamber wall thickness would be the minimum wall thickness multiplied by two.

Chamber Wall Thickness = 2 * (Min.Wall Thickness) = 2 * 0.054 = 0.108 inches

Checking our PVC pipe, we find that the wall thickness is 0.203 inches, which is well above 0.108 inches. We can calculate a safety factor using the equation below:

Safety Factor = (Actual thickness) / (Minimum required thickness) = 0.203/0.054

Safety Factor = 3.75

So we would have an actual safety factor of 3.75. This is more than adequate for our purposes.

Structural Properties of Different Materials
Table 7-1

Material	Allowable Stress (psi)	Ulti. Tensile Strength (psi)
Aluminum EC-O	4,000	12,000
Alum. 1100-O	5,000	13,000
Alum. 2014-T6	60,000	70,000
Alum. 6061-T6	40,000	45,000
C1020 Steel	48,000	75,000
304 Stainless Steel	35,000	85,000
316 Stainless Steel	30,000	80,000
PVC	--	7,450
Phenolic Grade XX	--	16,000/13,000
Phenolic Grade CE	--	9,000/7,000
Epoxy Laminate G-10	--	40,000/35,000
Durham's Water Putty	--	750 (Estimate)
Graphite	--	2,300 - 4,300 (70 F - Hot)

Nozzle Design and Structural Analysis

There are a variety different nozzles designs that can be used in a rocket motor. The first would be to make the entire nozzle out of one material, Figure 7-1. This nozzle can be bonded into the chamber for a single use or held in by a snap ring, retaining ring, pins or bolts. The

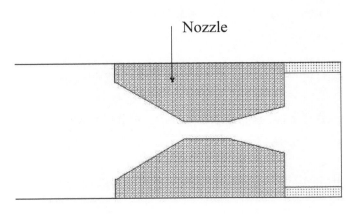

Figure 7-1: Rocket Nozzle Made Out of One Material

retaining ring can be bolted into place or screwed into the chamber where the chamber wall is threaded.

In many cases, the single piece nozzle is not acceptable such as when you use graphite with a long duration motor. The graphite will transmit too much heat into the chamber walls. So it must sit on a thermal insulating material. Also, the structural loads on a single material may be too great for the material such as graphite or phenolic. In this case the nozzle must be made out of a stronger material such as aluminum or steel. These materials cannot usually withstand the heat of the exhaust gases so they must be protected. In all of these cases, the nozzle must be made out of more than one material, Figure 7-2:

If you are using PVC pipe for the rocket chamber, you will probably go with PVC fittings to make the nozzle, Figure 7-3. In this case, you will have a multiple piece nozzle with the fitting filled with Durham`s water putty or similar material. In the case, where the water putty erodes too much for the motor, a graphite or phenolic insert can be used to reduce the throat erosion, Figure 7-4.

Regardless of the nozzle type, there are some basic fundamental approaches to analyzing these nozzles based on the ways nozzles fail. The first occurs when the nozzle wall thickness is insufficient to hold the motor pressure. The required thickness for the nozzle depends on the nozzle radius and throat radius. The following formula can be used to calculate the minimum nozzle wall thickness.

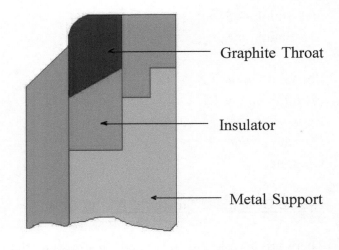

Graphite Throat

Insulator

Metal Support

Figure 7-2: Multiple Piece Nozzle With Different Materials

Min. nozzle wall thickness = t_n = Square root {[(k) x (MEOP) x ([Nozzle diameter/2])^2]/[Ultimate tensile strength]}

Figure 7-3: PVC Fitting Filled With a Single Material

For example, lets suppose our CE phenolic nozzle was going to be a solid piece inside the chamber. The phenolic nozzle will be one inch thick with a diameter of 2.5 inches. From Table 7-1, we use an average value for the ultimate tensile strength value of 8,000 psi. Recall, that the maximum expected chamber pressure for the motor is 300 psi. The only unknown in the equation is the value for k.

To determine the value of k, we need to ratio the nozzle diameter to the throat diameter. For our motor, the nozzle diameter is 2.5 inches and the throat radius is 0.32 inches. Then:

Nozzle diameter ratio = (Nozzle diameter) / (Throat diameter)

= 2.5/0.32 = 7.81

From Figure 7-5, we see that the value of k is approximately 2.30. We can now solve for the minimum nozzle wall thickness.

Min. nozzle wall thickness = tn = Square root {[(2.30) * (300) * (2.5/2)^2] / (8000)}

t_n = Square root {(2.30 * 300 * 1.5625) / (8000)} = Square root {1078.1 / 8000}

t_n = Square root (0.135) = 0.367 inches

From this we can see that our nozzle thickness of one inch is more than adequate. Suppose that instead of making the nozzle a solid piece of phenolic, we make the nozzle out of a PVC pipe transition fitting with water putty and a phenolic insert for the throat. We do not have to check the PVC fitting, as that is good for twice the rating of the 2.5 inch PVC pipe. The phenolic insert will sit on the lip of the PVC fitting. The PVC lip should

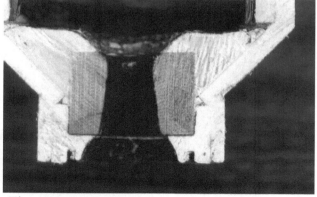

Figure 7-4: PVC Fitting With Two Materials - Durham's Water Putty and CE Phenolic

K - Coefficient

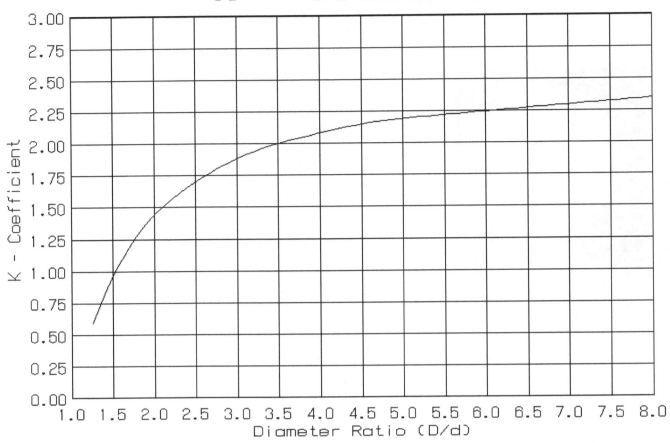

Figure 7-5: Stress Factor K as a Function of the Diameter Ratio

be good for twice the pressure rating so the failure mode for the nozzle would be a failure of the phenolic insert. For this situation we use the same equation as before for calculating the minimum nozzle wall thickness. In this case the nozzle insert will have a diameter of one inch and we want to know what is the minimum thickness we can make the insert. Then,

$$\text{Nozzle diameter ratio} = 1.0/0.32 = 3.125$$

From Figure 7-5, we see that k is approximately 1.90. Then:

$$t_n = \text{Square root} \{(1.90 * 300 * (1/2)^2) / 8000\} = \text{Square root} \{(1.90 * 300 * 0.25) / 8000\}$$

$$t_n = \text{Square root} \{142.5 / 8000\} = \text{Square root} (0.0178) = 0.133 \text{ inches}$$

Based on this result, we could make the phenolic insert very thin. From a practical standpoint, we would not want to make it any thinner than 0.25 inches.

Bulkhead Failure

Bulkheads are generally flat plates inserted inside the rocket chamber. They are held in place by a snap ring, retaining ring, pins or bolts. The other type of bulkhead is an insulated PVC end cap. They are good for twice the pressure rate of the PVC pipe and do not have to be structurally analyzed. In our example motor, we would use an insulated PVC end cap with the PVC pipe chamber.

However, to illustrate how to analyze a typical bulkhead, lets look at a 2.5 inch diameter aluminum bulkhead with a 3/8 inch diameter hole holding the delay charge. The minimum required bulkhead thickness can be calculated using the same equation as for calculating the minimum required nozzle thickness.

Min. bulkhead thickness = tb = Square root $\{[(k) \times (MEOP) \times ([Bulkhead\ diameter/2])^2]/[Ultimate\ tensile\ strength]\}$

We get the ultimate tensile strength from Table 7-1 and look up the value for k in Figure 7-5 based on the bulkhead ratio. If the bulkhead does not have an ejection delay charge or hole, the value for k is 1.24.

Bulkhead ratio = (Bulkhead diameter) / (Delay charge diameter)

Our bulkhead does have a delay charge so the bulkhead ratio is:

Bulkhead ratio = 2.5 / 0.375 = 6.66

Then the value for k is approximately 2.30. Finally, we can calculate the minimum thickness for the bulkhead.

$$t_b = Square\ root\ \{[2.30 * 300 * (2.50/2)^2] / (45000)]\}$$

$$t_b = Square\ root\ \{[2.30 * 300 * 1.5625]/45000\} = Square\ root\ \{1078/45,000\}$$

$$t_b = Square\ root\ \{0.02396\} = 0.15\ inches$$

This is the minimum thickness for the bulkhead. For safety, it would be good to double its thickness for a safety factor of two. Then, the bulkhead thickness would be:

Bulkhead Thickness = 2 * 0.15 = 0.30 inches

This is probably thinner than the required delay charge length. So, the required length for the delay grain will set the bulkhead thickness.

Nozzle and/or Bulkhead Loss

A major structural failure to examine is the potential for ejection of the nozzle or bulkhead. For a PVC pipe motor, you would use primer and PVC cement to hold the fittings onto the PVC pipe rocket chamber. With surface preparation as specified on the primer and cement cans, these bonds should not fail. Analysis is really not required, but we can take a quick look to illustrate how you would examine the strength of the bond.

First, you need to know the shear strength of the adhesive in the bond. We can calculate that by determining the force on the bulkhead and then dividing that by the adhesive surface area. The force on the bulkhead is the pressure multiplied by the cross-sectional surface area of the bulkhead:

Bulkhead ejection force = (MEOP) * (0.785) * (PVC pipe outer diameter)^2

The adhesive surface area is the circumference of the bulkhead multiplied by its thickness:

Adhesive surface area = 3.14 * (PVC pipe outer diameter) * (PVC cement bond length)

If we divide the bulkhead force by the adhesive surface area, then we will get an expression for the required adhesive strength:

Required adhesive strength = 0.25 * (MEOP) * (PVC pipe outer diameter) / (PVC cement bond length)

For example, let's say that the outer diameter of the chamber is 2.875 inches and depth of the PVC cement bond is 1.25 inches. Then we can calculate the minimum required shear strength of the adhesive by the following formula:

Required adhesive strength = (0.25 * 300 * 2.875) /1.25 = 215.6/1.25 = 172.5 psi

The PVC glue strength is good for about 500 psi. In this case, the adhesive has more than enough strength to hold fitting.

If you have a bulkhead that you are going to glue inside the rocket chamber, then the formula for the minimum required adhesive strength would be as follows:

$$\text{Min. required adhesive strength} = 0.25 * (\text{MEOP}) * (\text{Chamber inside diameter})/(\text{Cement bond length})$$

Retaining Pins or Bolts

The bulkhead and nozzle can be bonded into the chamber. For PVC pipe and fittings, mechanical fasteners are not necessary to hold them together. The PVC primer and glue are adequate. For other bonding systems and materials, it may be necessary to add retaining pins to ensure the nozzle and bulkhead are not blown out during the motor firing. To simply rely on epoxy to hold a four inch diameter aluminum bulkhead inside an aluminum chamber at 700 psi can provide unexpected thrills. So that you can properly design retaining pins or bolts for your future motors, if required, we have included this section on their design and sizing. The analysis approach applies whether you use a pin or bolt.

Let's look at a different motor design than the PVC pipe motor we have been examining, Figure 7-6. Suppose we have a motor made with an aluminum bulkhead and chamber. The MEOP is 700 psi and the inside diameter of the chamber is 4.00 inches and the outside diameter is 4.5 inches. Our design will use retaining pins to keep the bulkhead and nozzle from being ejected due to chamber pressure. We need to look at the strength of the pins and whether the pins will tear through the holes in the chamber. To make the design simpler, we will be using the same diameter retaining pins in the bulkhead as in the nozzle. The structural load on the bulkhead retaining pins is higher than those holding the nozzle. Consequently, we need only examine the retaining pins for the bulkhead.

We plan to use SAE 1020 steel retaining pins in the bulkhead and nozzle. For our motor, there will be six retaining pins for the nozzle and six retaining

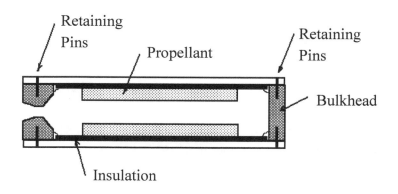

Figure 7-6: Solid rocket motor with retaining pins

pins for the bulkhead. To calculate the force on all the retaining pins in the bulkhead, we simply multiply the cross-sectional area of the bulkhead by the MEOP of the motor.

$$\text{Bulkhead Ejection Force} = \text{MEOP} * 0.785 * (\text{Bulkhead diameter})^2$$

$$\text{Bulkhead Ejection Force} = 700 * 0.785 * (4.0)^2 = 8,792 \text{ lbs!}$$

It may seem hard to believe, but there will be a force of a little less than 4.5 tons trying to pull the bulkhead out of the chamber. On every square inch inside the chamber, there is a maximum force of 700 lbs trying to push the rocket motor apart. While 700 psi is not a real high pressure, the force it creates inside the motor trying to tear things apart is not insignificant. If you can visualize this concept, it will save you many explosions in your motor testing. High chamber pressures and large diameter motors create very high ejection forces on the bulkhead and nozzle. If a bulkhead were 6 inches in diameter in a motor with a MEOP of 1000 psi, the bulkhead ejection load would be 28,260 lbs or 14 tons! Think about what would happen if that bulkhead were ejected during static testing.

There are going to be six retaining pins in our 4.5 inch motor. The bulkhead ejection force will be divided evenly among them:

$$\text{Retaining Pin Load} = (\text{Ejection Force})/(\text{Number of Pins}) = 8792/6 = 1,465 \text{ lbs}$$

The required minimum thickness of each pin can be calculated using the following equation:

$$\text{Min. Retaining Pin Radius} = r_p = \text{Square root } \{[\text{Retaining Pin Load}]/[3.14 * \text{ Ultimate Tensile Strength}]\}$$

$$r_p = \text{Square root } \{[1,465]/[3.14 * 75,000]\} = \text{Square root } \{1,465/235,500\}$$

$$r_p = \text{Square root } \{0.006221\} = 0.079 \text{ inches}$$

Then the minimum required retaining pin diameter is twice the radius of 0.079 or 0.158 inches. Using a safety factor of two, the retaining pins must have a radius of two times r_p.

$$\text{Retaining Pin Diameter} = 2 * 0.158 = 0.316 \text{ inches}$$

Suppose we feel this is a bit large for a retaining pin and would like to make them 0.25 inch in diameter. We could determine the safety factor for this size pin using the following:

Safety Factor = (Actual Pin Diameter)/(Min. Required Pin Diameter)

Safety Factor = 0.25/0.158 = 1.58

While this is less than the desired safety factor of two, it is still well above the minimum value of one. However, we could try adding another pin to make seven pins, which would reduce the required pin diameter so that we would be all right with 0.25 inch pins. Let`s say that we decide to stay with six pins and to go with 0.25 inch retaining pins.

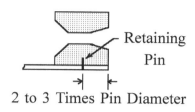

2 to 3 Times Pin Diameter

Figure 7-7: Retaining Pin Distance

Retaining Pin or Bolt Hole Location

It is good design practice to locate the retaining pins at least two to three hole diameters from the end of the chamber, Figure 7-7. For plastic chambers, the minimum hole distance should be three diameters. For metal chambers, it can be as small as two hole diameters. If the retaining pin holes are located closer to the chamber edge than the minimum distance specified above, the retaining pins could rip through the chamber wall, Figure 7-8.

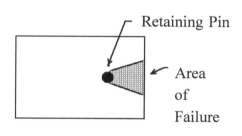

Figure 7-8: Retaining pin pull through failure

Our chamber is metal, so the minimum retaining pin hole distance should be at least two times the pin diameter. The retaining pin diameter is 0.25 inches. Then, the minimum hole distance is equal to 0.25 inches multiplied by two to yield 0.50 inches.

Now that you have sized the retaining pins or bolts, you need to look at stress where these pins or bolts go through the chamber. Since they weaken the chamber in the axial direction at each end. For our example, we have selected 6 retaining pins on each end of the chamber. The average chamber stress in the axial direction at the retaining pins is:

Average Axial Chamber Wall Stress = S_a = (Bulkhead ejection force)/(Wall area)

The axial force is greatest at the bulkhead so we will look at that location. The wall area is the wall thickness multiplied by the total amount of wall between all the retaining pins on one end.

Wall Area = (Wall Thickness) * [(3.14) * (Chamber Diameter) - (Number of Retaining Pins) * (Pin Diameter)]

Wall Area = (0.25) * [(3.14 * 4.0) - (6 * 0.25)] = 0.25 * [12.56 - 1.5]

Wall Area = 0.25 * 11.06 = 2.765 Inch^2

The bulkhead ejection force has already been calculated to be 8,792 lbs, so the average axial chamber wall stress is:

Average Axial Chamber Wall Stress = 8,792/2.765 = 3,180 psi

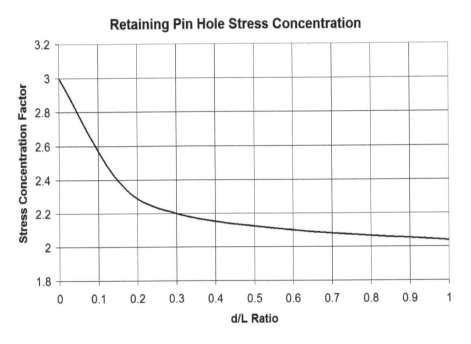

The tensile strength of the aluminum is 12,000 psi, Table 7-1. Since the average wall stress is 3,180 psi, it would appear that there is plenty of margin. However, at the retaining pin holes the stress is concentrated to a value higher than the average stress between the holes. The stress concentration factor is dependent on the ratio of the hole diameter to the distance between holes, Figure 7-9. The distance between holes is the chamber radius multiplied by the angle between holes. Our motor has six retaining pins at each end that are 0.25 inches in diameter.

Figure 7-9: Stress concentration factor at retaining pin/bolt holes

Distance between holes = L = 3.14 * (Chamber Diameter)/(Number of Holes)

Distance between holes = L = (3.14 * 4.0)/6 = 2.09 inches

We can combine this with the retaining pin diameter to get the ratio of the hole diameter to distance between holes. With this ratio, we can go into Figure 7-5 and get the stress concentration factor.

Ratio of the Retaining Pin Diameter to Distance Between Holes = d/L = 0.25/2.09 = 0.12

From Figure 7-8, we find that the stress concentration factor is approximately 2.5. Then, the axial chamber stress at each bulkhead retaining pin hole is 3,180 psi multiplied by 2.5 to equal 7,950 psi.

Maximum Axial Chamber Wall Stress = (Stress concentration factor) * (Average Axial Chamber Stress)

Maximum Axial Chamber Wall Stress = 2.5 * 3,180 = 7,950 psi

The safety factor is the ultimate tensile strength divided by the maximum axial chamber wall stress or 12,000 divided by 7950 to equal 1.62 (12,000/7950 = 1.62). While our safety factor is not greater than two, it is adequate. With the structural analysis of our motor completed, we're ready to move on to the next step of thermally examining the motor.

Figure 7-10: Retaining Ring and Bolts

Retaining Rings

Another way to hold the nozzle and bulkhead into place is to use a retaining ring along with pins or bolts, Figure 7-10. In this case, you need to also look at the thickness of the ring using the same equations in the previous section with the following adjustments:

Average axial ring wall stress = Sa = (Bulkhead ejection force)/(Ring wall area)

Bulkhead ejection force = (3.14/4) * (MEOP) * (Chamber inside diameter)

Ring wall area = (Ring thickness) * [(3.14) * (Ring diameter) - (Number of retaining pins) * (Pin diameter)]

Distance between holes = L = 3.14 * (Retaining ring diameter)/(Number of holes)

Maximum axial Retaining ring stress = (Stress concentration factor) * (Average axial ring wall stress)

Snap rings

In some motors, you may want to use a snap ring to hold the nozzle and bulkhead into place. The snap ring is held inside the chamber by the groove or ridge machined into the chamber. The stress on the snap ring is:

Snap ring stress = (Bulkhead ejection force) / (3.14 * [Snap ring thickness] * [Chamber inside diameter])

Suppose the snap ring thickness is 0.1 inches, the chamber inside diameter is three inches and the bulkhead ejection force is 3500 lbs. Then, snap ring stress is:

Snap ring stress = 3500 / (3.14 * 0.1 * 3.0) = 3500 / 0.972 = 3715 psi

This is low enough for standard carbon steel, but we would be very close to the allowable stress for low grade aluminum.

For the depth of the snap ring groove, you size it based on the stress the ring creates in the chamber. Use the following equation for that:

Snap ring stress in chamber = (Bulkhead ejection force) / {(3.14/4) * ([Chamber outside diameter]^2 - [Groove diameter]^2)}

Groove diameter = (Chamber inside diameter) + (2 * [Groove depth])

Let us the same example and make the groove depth equal to 0.07 inches, the groove width is slight bigger than the snap ring at 0.12 inches and the outside diameter of the chamber is 3.25 inches. Then,

Groove diameter = 3 + (2 * 0.07) = 3.14 inches

Snap ring stress in chamber = (3500) / {0.785* [(3.25)^2 - (3.14)^2]}

= 3500 / (0.785 * [10.5625 - 9.8596]) = 3500 / (0.785 * 0.7029) = 3500/0.552

Snap ring stress in chamber = 6341 psi

This stress level is too high for the lower grades of aluminum, but is very low compared to the allowable stress for 6061 aluminum. So, if we were going to use aluminum for the chamber, we would use 6061 aluminum.

Sealing with o-rings

An o-ring works by it squeezing flat against two surfaces and thus providing a seal. The amount of compression should be about 10% of the o-rings thickness. That 10% of compression will provide a sealing surface area 40% to 45% of the o-ring diameter, Figure 7-11. When the motor is pressurized, the seal moves inside the groove as shown in Figure 7-12. If the gap between the o-ring groove and the other part is too great, the o-ring can be extruded between the space. While the o-ring may not completely come out through the gap, it will become damaged and may not seal.

Figure 7-11: O-ring Under Compression in Groove

The first question in selecting an o-ring is, "How big should the diameter be?" The answer is the bigger the better as the larger the o-ring the more surface area is available to provide a seal. Suppose we have a rocket chamber with an inside diameter of three inches and we have a removable bulkhead. We will make the o-ring grooves in the bulkhead rather than the chamber as the o-ring grooves would weaken the chamber walls. The chamber pressure for the motor will be 600 psi. The first thing to do is to determine the maximum gap that can exist between the bulkhead wall and the rocket chamber wall. We do that by going to Figure 7-12. It shows the maximum allowable gap as a function of pressure and the hardness of the o-ring.

Suppose the o-ring material we select has a shore hardness of 70. The 0-ring supplier provides the o-ring hardness. While our chamber pressure is expected to be no greater than 600 psi, it would probably be a good idea to design the o-ring for a slightly higher pressure to provide a safety factor. Lets design it for 900 psi. From Figure 7-13, we see that the gap between the rocket chamber wall and bulkhead cannot be

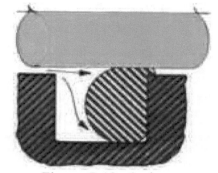

Figure 7-12: O-ring Compressed in Groove Under Pressure

greater than 0.010 inches.   Let's selected an o-ring diameter of $1/8^{th}$ inch or 0.125 inches. Then the depth of the o-ring groove in the bulkhead is:

O-ring groove depth = (0.9 * O-ring diameter) - (Gap between chamber wall & bulkhead)

Then:

O-ring groove depth = (0.9 * 0.125) - 0.01 = 0.1025 inches

The bulkhead diameter must be machined to:

Bulkhead diameter = (Chamber inside diameter) - [2 * (Gap between chamber wall & bulk-head)]

In our case:

Bulkhead diameter = 3.00 - (2 * 0.01) = 3.00 - 0.002 = 2.98 inches

The width of the o-ring groove should be wide enough so that the o-ring can move freely in the groove. A good rule of thumb is to make the width about 0.10 inches wider than the o-ring diameter.

O-ring groove width = W = (O-ring diameter) + 0.10

In our case, the o-ring groove width would be:

O-ring groove width = 0.125 + 0.10 = 0.225 inches

The groove would be machined into the bulkhead so that the side walls of the groove can be vertical or tapered five degrees off vertical. The corners of the groove can also be rounded to a radius of 0.005 inches.

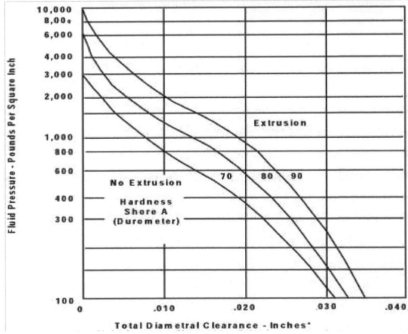

Figure 7-13: O-ring Extrusion as a Function of Clearance Gap

Motor Thermal Analysis
Chapter 8

The final step in the design process is to thermally examine the motor. The general areas to be examined are the nozzle, chamber walls and bulkhead. The analysis will be done using the included thermo-ablation computer program, entitled THERM. The thermal analysis consists of one-dimensional thermal cuts through the nozzle. The analysis is one-dimensional because it is assumed that the heat flows only in one direction. Figure 8-1 shows the difference between a one-dimensional and two-dimensional analysis. For materials that act as insulators, the one-dimensional assumption is not bad. Materials such as plastics and rubbers are thermal insulators. The one-dimensional assumption is less valid for graphite, which conducts heat fairly well.

The locations of the thermal cuts in a typical motor are shown in Figure 8-2. While all these thermal analysis cuts may be necessary to properly analyze a motor, there are only two that are really important. The first location is adjacent to the chamber wall just before the nozzle entrance region. This point is important because it will determine if the rubber insulation thickness is adequate. The second location is at the nozzle throat. This location will give an estimate of the throat erosion, which will greatly affect the performance of the motor.

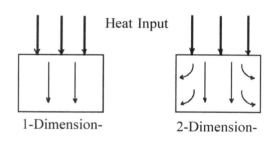

Figure 8-1: One & Two Dimensional Heat Transfer Analysis

Chamber Insulation

Before we can run the THERM program, we need to determine the input values to the program. The first value is the temperature of the propellant combustion gas. Our CHEM computer run has already determined the chamber temperature to be 3400° F. For the calculations and computer program, the temperature must be expressed in absolute temperature. This is done by adding 460 to the Fahrenheit temperature to convert it into degrees Rankine.

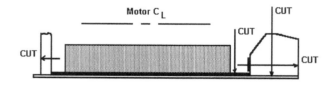

Figure 8-2: Typical Location of Thermal Cuts

$$T_{chamber} = 3418° \text{ F} + 460 = 3878° \text{ R}$$

The next value to calculate is the heat transfer coefficient. This number determines the amount of heat transferred to the nozzle wall. It can be calculated using the following equation:

$$\text{Heat Transfer Coefficient} = h = (k/\text{Diameter}) * 0.023 * Re^{0.8} * Pr^{0.4}$$

For all the propellant formulations, we will assume the Prandtl number, Pr, to be 0.49. The value for the gas conductivity, k, will be equal to 0.218 Btu/Hr-Ft-R. The value for "Diameter" is simply the diameter of the motor chamber, as we are not going to use rubber insulation inside the chamber. In our case, it would be 2.5 inches. To be consistent with our units of measure, we must convert 2.50 inches into feet. This is done by dividing 2.50 inches by 12 to equal 0.208 ft.

The Reynolds number, Re, can be calculated from the following equation:

$$\text{Reynolds number} = Re = [(\text{Gas density}) * (\text{Gas velocity}) * (\text{Diameter})]/(\text{Viscosity})$$

Again, we have introduced some more parameters to be calculated, but don't panic, it won't be that hard to determine them. The value for "Viscosity" will be 0.000062 lb/ft-sec for all propellant formulations. The next parameter is gas density, which can be calculated using the following equation:

$$\text{Gas Density} = (\text{Chamber pressure})/[(\text{Gas constant}) * (\text{Gas temperature})]$$

From our FPRED run, we know that the average chamber pressure for the motor is 120 psi. To make the units of measure consistent in our calculations, the chamber pressure must be converted to units of psia or absolute pressure. This is done by adding 14.7 to the average chamber pressure printed in the output of FPRED. For our example, we would add 14.7 to 120 psi to obtain 134.7 psia. We can round this up to an even 135 psia average chamber pressure. The gas constant is 1545 divided by the molecular weight of the propellant gas. The molecular weight for our formulation is found in CHEM. It is 20.8. Then the gas constant is 1545 divided by 20.8 or 74.3. We are now ready to calculate the gas density in the rocket chamber.

$$\text{Gas Density} = (135 * 144)/(74.3 * 3878) = 19440/288135 = 0.067 \text{ lb/ft}^3$$

It should be noted that in the above calculation the pressure was multiplied by 144 to convert the units from square inches to square feet so that all units would be consistent. This value is always used in the calculation when the chamber pressure is expressed in units of psia.

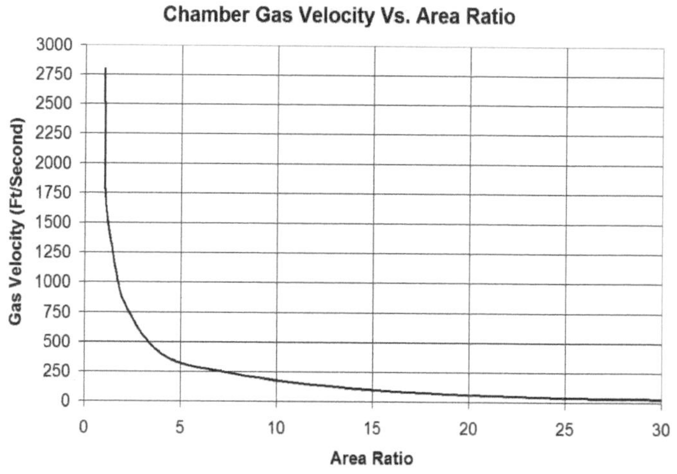

Chamber Gas Velocity Vs. Area Ratio

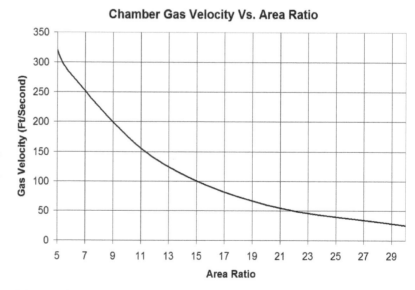

Figure 8-3: Gas Velocity in Motor Chamber

The final parameter to determine is the gas velocity at the location of our thermal analysis cut. The first step is to determine the ratio of the chamber cross-sectional area to the throat area using the following equation:

$$\text{Area Ratio} = (\text{Diameter/Throat diameter})^2$$

$$\text{Area Ratio} = (2.50/0.32)^2 = (7.8125)^2 = 61.04$$

With the area ratio known, we can go to Figure 8-3 or Figure 8-4 and find the gas velocity directly in ft/second. From Figure 8-4, it appears that the gas velocity may be as low as 10 ft/second. Now, we are ready to calculate Re.

$$\text{Re} = (0.067 * 10 * 0.208)/0.000062 = 0.139/0.000062 = 2042$$

We can then calculate the heat transfer coefficient using the equation stated earlier.

$$\text{Heat Transfer Coefficient.} = h = (0.218/0.208) * 0.023 * (2042)^{0.8} * (0.49)^{0.4}$$

Heat Transfer Coefficient. = h = 1.05 * 0.023 * 445 * 0.752

Heat Transfer Coefficient. = h = 8.1 Btu/Hr-Ft^2-R

For our ablation program, we will need to convert the units to Btu/Second-Ft^2-R by dividing the previous answer by 3600.

Heat Transfer. Coefficient. = h = 8.1/3600 = 0.002 Btu/Sec-Ft^2-R

Chamber Gas Velocity Vs. Area Ratio

Figure 8-4: Gas Velocity in Motor Chamber from Area Ratio 5 to 30

Okay, you can let your brain and calculator cool off now. You've done the hard part in setting up the input for the thermal ablation program. The final parameters to be set up for the program are the thicknesses of the materials and the corresponding thermal material properties. For our motor, the PVC wall thickness is 0.20 inches. The thermal material properties required by the computer program are shown in Table 8-1. Inputting these values into the program as shown in the user's manual, we can run THERM to determine the insulation ablation and temperature distribution through the nozzle.

Material Thermal Properties
Table 8-1

Material	Density (lb/ft)	Cp (Btu/lbm-R)	k(Btu/hr-ft-R)	Melt Temp(F)	Heat of Fusion (Btu/lbm)
Nylon	71.0	0.40	0.100	480	4210
PVC	86.0	0.40	0.085	300	2100
ATJ Graphite	108.0	0.40	25.0	3800 (Ablates)	2200
G-90 Graphite	118.0	0.40	36.0	3800 (Ablates)	2750
EPDM	70.0	0.40	0.155	1000 (Ablates)	2200
EC-O Alum.	169.0	0.23	135.0	1195	170
6061-T6 Alum.	169.0	0.23	99.0	1140	170
C1020 Steel	489.0	0.11	27.0	2750	200
304 Stainless	501.0	0.12	9.4	2750	200
Water Putty (est.)	115.0	0.40	0.67	3000 (Ablates/shears)	750
CE Phenolic (est.)	71.0	0.40	0.30	2300 (Ablates)	2700

The results show that the PVC pipe starts melting in about three seconds, but only 0.002 inches of PVC is ablated away. So, the motor will be fine without insulation inside the chamber.

Thermal Cut at Nozzle Throat

The procedure for making the nozzle throat cut is the same as used for the internal insulation. The thermal boundary conditions are also determined the same way except for the gas velocity. It is always sonic or Mach 1. From CHEM, we see that the sonic gas velocity is 2858 ft/second.

The gas temperature at the nozzle throat has to be calculated using the chamber gas temperature and the gas free stream temperature. The gas free stream temperature is 90% of the chamber temperature. The following equation can be used to calculate the gas temperature at the throat:

$$\text{Gas Throat Temperature} = T_t = T_f + (P_r)^{0.33} * (T_c - T_f)$$

Chamber Temperature = Tc = 3878° R

Free stream Temperature = Tf = (Tc * 0.9) = 3878 * 0.9 = 3490° R

Recall that Pr equals 0.49 so that the gas throat temperature is:

Gas Throat Temperature = Tt = 3490 + $(0.49)^{0.33}$ * (3878 - 3490)

Throat gas temperature = Tt = 3490 + (0.79) * (388) = 3490 + 307 = 3797° R

We will estimate the heat transfer coefficient in the throat region using the same procedures and equations as before. However, if you have a large amount of throat erosion during the firing, you should calculate the heat transfer coefficient for the initial and end of firing throat diameters. The reason for doing this is that the change to a larger throat diameter will cause the heat transfer coefficient to drop. If you keep the initial higher value, you will over predict the throat erosion.

In order to calculate the heat transfer coefficient, you need to calculate the gas density at the throat. The gas density will always be less than the chamber density by a factor of 0.62. We know from past experience that the throat erosion will be low and the motor firing time is relatively short.   So we are only going to use the initial throat diameter for our calculations. Then the throat gas density is as follows:

Throat Gas Density = (Chamber Gas Density) * 0.62 = 0.06 * 0.62

Throat Gas Density = 0.0372 lb/ft^3

Diameter will now be the throat diameter for calculating the Reynolds number. We need to convert the 0.32 inch throat diameter to feet by dividing it by 12 to yield 0.027 ft. Then, we calculate the value for Re using the same equation as before:

Re = (0.0372 * 2,858 * 0.027)/0.000062 = 2.87/0.000062 = 46,290

Then, the heat transfer coefficient is as follows:

Heat Transfer Coefficient = h = (0.218/0.027) * 0.023 * $(46290)^{0.8}$ * $(0.49)^{0.4}$

Heat Transfer Coefficient = h = 8.07 * 0.023 * 5400 * 0.75

$$\text{Heat Transfer Coefficient} = h = 752 \text{ (Btu/Hr-Ft}^2\text{-R)} \text{ or } 0.21 \text{ (Btu/Sec-Ft}^2\text{-R)}$$

Running the THERM computer program at the throat with the calculated heat transfer coefficient and throat gas temperature shows that the ablation of the throat in the radial direction is 0.08 inches. For a 9 second burn, that gives a throat erosion rate of 0.009 inches per second or 9 mils/second. In our ballistic analysis, we assumed a throat erosion of 0.012 inches/second or 12 mils/second. With less throat erosion, we will have a higher chamber pressure. We will look at that in the next chapter.

Thermal Cut Through Bulkhead

The last point to look at in our design is the bulkhead or end cap. The bulkhead is PVC with a layer of 1/16 inch EPDM insulation. The gas temperature at the bulkhead will be the same as the chamber gas temperature, 3878° R. We can assume that the heat transfer coefficient is the same as for the chamber insulation since the flow conditions are very similar. As you may recall, the heat transfer coefficient was 0.002 Btu/Sec-Ft^2-R for the insulation. This value is actually be a little high since the flow of the gas at the bulkhead will be virtually zero. Since we know the chamber was fine without insulation, we could reasonability assume that the bulkhead would be fine without insulation as well. However, it would be wise to put a thin layer of insulation there as the igniter could cause a very local hot spot. So, while the analysis shows we do not need the insulation, to be on the safe side, we will put in a thin layer of rubber.

The motor appears to thermally sound and should function as designed with respect to temperatures. However, the throat erosion was a little less than originally designed for and it would be wise to rerun FPRED with the new value.

Final Rocket Motor Design
Chapter 9

Now that we have completed our ballistic, thermal and structural analysis, we must verify that all our assumptions are compatible. This means that all material thicknesses, materials, erosion rates, pressures, etc. must be consistent or very close in all three analyses. If the assumptions are not compatible, then the analyses must be rerun until they are. Our assumptions appear to be consistent in all the analyses except the ballistic analysis where we used 12 mils/second instead of 9 mils/second. Rerunning FPRED with all input parameters the same as before except the throat erosion, we see that the maximum chamber pressure increases only by a very small amount. This change is not significant enough to redo the stress and thermal analysis. Consequently, we will say the motor design is adequate and ready for testing. Our motor design is now summarized in Table 9-1

Motor Final Design Parameters
Table 9-1

- Initial thrust = 36.3 lbs
- Average thrust = 26.7 lbs
- Throat diameter = 0.32 inch
- Exit cone diameter = 0.5845 inch
- Average chamber pressure = 183 psia
- Thrust duration = 6.8 seconds
- Total impulse = 181.7 lb-seconds
- Motor weight = 1.78 lbs
- Propellant weight = 0.89 lbs
- CE Phenolic nozzle
- 2.5 inch PVC pipe chamber
- Two segments of propellant cast into 2 inch PVC pipe
- Length of propellant segment = 3.0 inches
- Bore diameter = 0.625 inches

Nozzle and Exit Cone Design

We have calculated the nozzle throat diameter and exit cone diameter. The next question is what should be the contour of the nozzle going from the rocket chamber to the throat and out to the exit cone. The contour from the rocket chamber to the throat can be a straight cone at an angle of around 45 degrees. This angle is not really that important. Any reasonably smooth contour from the rocket chamber to the nozzle throat will work fine.

The contour of critical importance is the exit cone. An improper contour can result in shock layer formation, which causes a performance loss. The easiest exit cone contour is a straight cone. It can provide a shock-free expansion of the exhaust gases. The angle of the cone should be 15 degrees. That expands the gases with an acceptable amount of divergence loss. What is divergence loss?

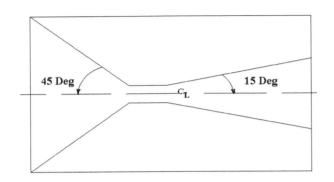

Figure 9-1: Entrance Region and Exit Cone for a Rocket Nozzle

As the gases flow through the exit cone they move in the axial direction, which provides thrust, but the gases also move in the radial direction. The movement of the gases in the radial direction as they leave the exit cone does not provide thrust and is a loss. The divergence loss factor for a straight cone is defined as follows:

Straight cone divergence loss factor = [1 + cosine (Cone angle)] /2.0

Thrust = (Straight cone divergence loss factor) * (Theoretical thrust)

If the cone angle is zero degrees, then the loss factor is one and there are no divergence losses. If the cone angle is 15 degrees, the divergence loss factor is 0.983 so the thrust is reduced by about 2% of its theoretical value. So for our motor we will make the exit cone at a 15-degree angle, Figure 9-1.

Straight cone divergence loss factor = [1 + cosine (15 degrees)] /2.0 = (1+0.966)/2

Straight cone divergence loss factor = 1.966/2 = 0.983

Cost of the Rocket Motor

At this point, we may want to estimate the cost of our motor to see if we want to build it or not. The major cost item is typically the propellant. A rule of thumb is $10 per pound, which includes shipping costs. We have 0.89 lbs of propellant, which yields a cost of about $8.90. The PVC nozzle fitting and end cap are about $5.00. The PVC pipe would be a couple dollars per foot for a chamber cost of about $2. The water putty consumed for the throat insert would be no more than $1.00 and the CE phenolic insert would be about $1.75. Your total cost to build this motor would be:

- Propellant = $8.90
- Nozzle/Bulkhead = $5
- PVC chamber = $2
- Water putty = $1
- CE phenolic insert = $1.75

Total Motor Cost = $18.65 (2.5 Inch J-119 Motor)

The important thing to remember is that the design of a rocket motor is a trial and error process. Rarely, will the first design be the one meets all your needs. You must decide what is important to you and how much you are willing to pay for it.

Making Rocket Chambers
Chapter 10

After you have finished designing the motor and have all the required dimensions, it is time to starting making your rocket motor. If you are going to make it out of metal, you can buy pipe or tubing close to the dimensions you want. The diameter specified for pipe refers to the inside diameter. The diameter referred to for tubing refers to the outside diameter.

Pipe outer diameter = (Pipe diameter) + (2 * [Wall thickness])

Tube inside diameter = (Tube diameter) - (2 * [Wall thickness])

Cut the metal tube to the desired length using a hacksaw or band saw. A band saw will do a better cut. The chamber length should be equal to:

Rocket chamber length = (Propellant length) + (Bulkhead thickness) + (Nozzle thickness) + (Bulkhead retaining ring width) + (Nozzle retaining ring width)

If you are not going to be using retaining rings, but will be bonding the bulkhead and nozzles into the chamber, then those terms will be zero. If you are using a snap ring instead of a retaining ring, the use the following formula:

Rocket chamber length = (Propellant length) + (Bulkhead thickness) + (Nozzle thickness) + [3* (Bulkhead snap ring width)] + [3* (Nozzle snap ring width)]

The first step is to cut the tube or pipe to the proper length. Mark it for the desired chamber length. I would recommend making the chamber length about one inch longer than the propellant length for all propellant grain patterns except those that are segmented in uninsulated PVC pipe. This allows the gases on the forward and aft ends to flow easily into the propellant bore or nozzle entrance region. For segmented patterns or propellant cartridges in uninsulated PVC pipe, I would recommend making the chamber length about 0.125 inches longer.

To make a square cut, you can "eye ball" it or use a mitre box and saw. These can be purchased at any store where tools are sold. The upper limit of a typical mitre box is two inch diameter pipe. You will have to start the cut above the guide grooves in the mitre box, so be careful. Once you get a little ways into the pipe, the saw will be in the mitre box grooves and the cut will be square. Don't worry if the cut is not quite square, this can be adjusted later with a file, if you want. For pipes over 3 inches in diameter, you will have to use a handsaw and cut it as square as you can. Again, the cut can be squared up with a file.

If you have an electric mitre saw, cutting large plastic diameter pipes is easy. While electric mitre saws can cost a couple hundred dollars, it could be a good investment if you plan to make a lot of motors 3 inches or larger in diameter. If you have a band saw, that is probably the best tool for cutting your chamber pipe or tube. It can cut metal and plastic depending on the band saw blade being used in it. The main thing is to try and make the cut as square as possible. The next step after you have cut the chamber is to file the ends smooth and remove any burrs from the cutting process. A combination rasp and flat file can be purchased from most hardware stores, it will make quick work of this task.

Chamber Insulation - Paper or Rubber?

Sometimes, you will have to insulate the chamber with a sheet of rubber insulation. For most of the PVC motors listed in Appendix A, you can skip the insulation. For those motors, the phenolic sleeve of the propellant cartridge is sufficient insulation for the pipe. You may have designed a motor that does not require insulation. In that case, just cut the pipe to the required length and you are done.

If you need to insulate the chamber, you can use rubber insulation sheets or in many cases cardboard tubes. Cardboard tubes are often used in metal case motors and sometimes in PVC pipe motors. In this case, select a cardboard tube that has an outer diameter just slightly smaller than the inside diameter of the chamber. The propellant cartridges then slide inside the insulation cardboard tube. The thickness of the cardboard tube should be around 1/16 of an inch. The insulation tubes are not bonded to the motor chamber so they can be replaced after each motor firing.

EPDM rubber is another good insulation that can be used in the chamber. It is available commercially in rolls of various thicknesses. When ordering insulation make sure that it is fully cured. Uncured insulation is useless for this application.

Installing Rubber Insulation

The first step is to mark your sheet of insulation with the required dimensions for your motor using a marking pen, ruler and straight edge. The rubber sheet can easily be cut to the proper size using the same hand shears that are used for cutting sheet metal. Cut the insulation with your hand shears, making the cut as straight as possible. After cutting the insulation, curl the insulation into the shape of a tube several times so that it bends easily.

Insert the insulation into the rocket chamber as far as you can. You may not be able to insert it all the way at this point. If not, look inside the chamber and see if the width of the insulation is too large causing the ends to overlap and the insulation to bind up. If so, remove the insulation from the chamber and trim it slightly. Reinsert it into the chamber and check the width again. It is important that the ends of the insulation do not overlap in the width direction. Don't worry if there is a gap between the insulation width ends which exposes PVC pipe, that will be filled in later with high temperature RTV. However, do try to minimize the gap width.

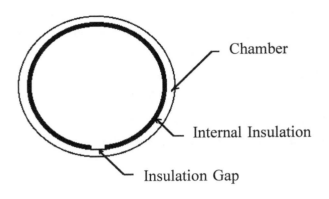

Figure 10-1: Internal Insulation Gap

If rubber insulation fits all the way into the chamber without the ends overlapping in the width direction, you are now ready to permanently insulate the chamber. First, work the insulation inside the chamber so that the insulation ends in the lengthwise direction are square with each other. A helpful hint is to keep the end of the insulation even with the end of the chamber. This enables you to use the end of the chamber as a guide. Once the insulation is square with the end of the chamber, push it into the chamber using a rod. The insulation will easily slide into the chamber and stay square.

The final step is to fill in the gap between the internal insulation ends in the width direction, Figure 10-1. This is done with RTV silicone rubber that can be purchased in automotive shops or home building supply stores. Open the tube of RTV silicone rubber and squeeze a big glob onto a rod or long screwdriver. Insert the rod to the mid-point of the chamber and push the glob of silicone rubber into the gap. Put more silicone rubber on the end of the rod and work your way, a glob at a time, from the mid-section to one end of the internal insulation. Do the same thing from the mid-section to the other end of the insulation.

It is important that the silicone rubber fills the entire gap with no voids or exposed bare chamber walls in the gap. Fill the gap until the top of the silicone rubber is even with internal

Clean
Away
RTV

insulation. The silicone rubber exposed surface will be uneven, but this is ok. A round rod works best for smoothing it out, but it will still be somewhat uneven. The important thing is that the silicone rubber thickness in the gap be the same thickness as the internal insulation.

Figure 10-2: Insulating PVC Chamber Joint

During the process of putting the RTV silicone rubber into insulation gap, you will probably get some on other places inside the chamber and the lip of the chamber. Clean these areas as best you can with a rod and paper towels.

If your chamber is made of PVC pipe, make sure there is no silicone rubber on the inside surfaces of the PVC pipe where the nozzle or bulkhead will be located in the motor. It is also important to clean any silicone rubber away from the lip of the internal insulation next to the PVC pipe, Figure 10-2. Use a screwdriver and paper towel to clean away any excess silicone rubber. When the nozzle and bulkheads are inserted into the chamber during final assembly, there must not be any silicone rubber interfering with that insertion.

Making Nozzles and Bulkheads
Chapter 11

Bulkheads that are PVC end caps and nozzles made from Durham`s Water Putty cast into plastic fittings makes the bulkheads and nozzles fairly easy to make and machine. You can insert graphite or phenolic into the water putty for a more erosion resistant throat material. For some motors, you may want to make the bulkhead out of metal or even the nozzle support out of metal.

<u>Making Nozzles</u>

For the nozzle throat and insulation, you can use Durham`s Water Putty, which can found in almost any hardware or home improvement store. While the putty holds up to the heat of the exhaust gases very well, it doesn`t have much structural strength. For one inch motors, it does have enough strength to withhold typical chamber pressures. For larger diameter motors, it is recommended that the water putty be cast into a plastic fittings or otherwise structurally supported to prevent crumbling of the nozzle due to pressure.

For all nozzle sizes, the Durham`s Water Putty is mixed or prepared in the same way. First, scoop out the dry powder in a quantity that is sufficient to do the nozzle or a number of nozzles. Put the powder into a paper cup. The water you add to the dry powder will compact a lot, so make sure you scoop out enough powder. After you make a few nozzles, you will have a better feel for the amount of powder.

When you have the right amount of powder in your paper cup, add small amounts of water to the powder and stir it in. You can always add water, but you can`t take it out. Be careful on adding the water, as you do not want too much. The consistency of the water putty mix should be like mortar or concrete. After you have mixed the water putty to this consistency, you are ready to cast it into your prepared fitting. The water putty works like cement and starts to "set-up" after mixing so don`t take a lunch break after you mix the water putty. Get it into the prepared fitting.

For the one inch PVC pipe motor, you will use a thread coupler to hold the water putty, Figure 11-1. This coupler has a smooth end that fits on the PVC pipe. The other end is threaded. The water putty is cast into the threaded part so that the threads can hold onto the putty to prevent it from being blown out during motor operation. Put a piece of duct tape over the open threaded end of the coupler so that the putty cannot flow out when it is put into the fitting. With the open end up on a table, scoop small amounts of water putty into the fitting

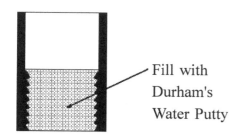

Fill with
Durham's
Water Putty

Figure 11-1: 1 Inch Threaded PVC
Fitting Filled with Durham's Water

and work it towards the bottom. It is important that you work the putty by tamping it into place so as to minimize voids or trapped air. Fill the fitting just to the point where the threads end.

For 1.5 to 2.5 inch PVC pipe motors, a transitional fitting is filled with the water putty. These fittings have a smooth end that goes over the PVC pipe and a small diameter open on the other end to accept a smaller PVC pipe. For 1.5 and 2.0 inch diameter fittings, the other end should be threaded to accept a 3/4 inch PVC pipe, Figure 11-2. As with the one inch coupler, put a piece of duct tape over the thread end of the fitting. Scoop water putty into the open end of the fitting a spoonful at a time and work to the bottom of the thread end. Fill the entire fitting with water putty. As with the one inch fitting, the threads will hold the water putty and keep it from being ejected during the firing.

If you start making larger motors in the three and four inch diameter range, you will need a transitional section to get from the larger pipe diameter down to a size where another threaded transitional section can be used. As shown in Figure 11-3, these transitional fittings go from three or four inch diameter PVC pipe to 1.5 or 2.0 inch PVC pipe. You can use for the nozzle blank either the 1.5 or 2.0 inch threaded transitional fittings as mentioned for the 1.5 or

Figure 11-2: 2 Inch PVC Fittings Filled with
Durham's Water Putty

2.0 inch motors. The small end of these transitional fittings may be larger than 3/4 inch since the throat size for larger motors often approaches or exceeds 3/4 inch. In this case, you may want a one inch, threaded smaller end. As before, put duct tape over the threaded end of the fitting. Working a spoonful of water putty at a time, fill the entire fitting with putty.

Drilling a Pilot Hole in the Nozzle Blank

Regardless of the fitting size, let it stand for two days at room temperature before you go on to the next step. The water putty should begin to turn a lighter shade of tan as it cures.

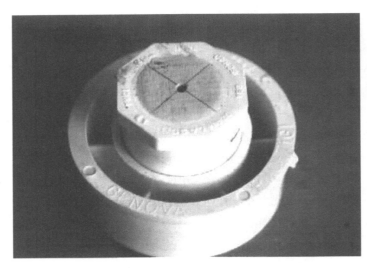

Figure 11-3: 3 Inch PVC Transitional Fitting With 3/4 Inch PVC Fitting - Filled With Water Putty

After two days, take your blank nozzle and mark the center of it with a pencil. It is important to find the center as closely as possible. Otherwise, the thrust from your motor will be off center producing a side thrust on your rocket. A simple way of finding the center is with a drawing compass. Set the compass to the radius of the blank nozzle. Then, take the pointed end of the compass and put it on the edge the blank. Draw an arc through the center of the blank using the compass. Do the same thing on the opposite side of the blank. Finally, do the same thing on the two sides. The arcs will touch each other exactly in the center of the blank, Figure 11-4. Make a mark at that point.

At the mark, drill out a 1/8 inch diameter hole with an electric drill or drill press. This pilot hole will permit air to get to the center of the water putty and let it dry out faster. If you have a forced air oven, you can put the fitting into it so that it will dry even faster. Otherwise, it may take about two weeks at room temperature for it to dry enough that you can do final machining on the nozzle blank.

Machining the Nozzle Blank

The next step is to drill out the nozzle throat. Take a drill bit that is the size of the throat. It is best to buy a large set of bits that are marked in thousands of an inch. It is important that the bit match the throat diameter as closely as possible. An actual throat hole smaller than what the motor was designed for can result in an explosion.

It is best to use a drill press to make the throat. If you don't have one, you could buy an attachment for your power drill that converts it into a drill press. The important thing is that the throat hole must be

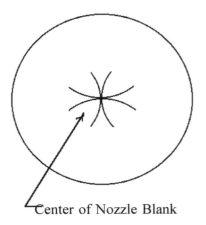

Center of Nozzle Blank

Figure 11-4: A Simple Way to Find the Nozzle Center

parallel to the centerline of the nozzle and hence the motor, Figure 11-5. If the throat hole is at an angle, then the thrust of the motor will produce a side thrust on your rocket. If you must drill it by hand with your electric drill, put the blank nozzle in a vise and carefully drill the hole. If your throat hole is not exactly parallel to the centerline, but slightly off, don't panic. It will probably be ok. Just do the best you can and don't rush this step. It is important.

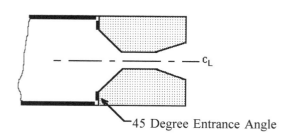

Figure 11-5: Entrance Region of Nozzle

Now, that the throat hole is drilled into the blank nozzle, it is time to make the exit cone. This is very simple. You can use a conical rotary rasp bit. These can be purchased in hardware stores. Put the bit into your electric drill and simply drill out the exit cone. It will easily drill out the water putty and make a nice cone. If you find that a lot of water putty is sticking to the rasp, the putty is probably too wet. Let it dry for a few more days and then try again. You should get mostly powder as you drill if it is properly dry.

The next step in making your nozzle is to cut out the entrance region. That is the area where the combustion gases from the chamber enter the nozzle. This should be a large cone cut at about a 45 degree angle, Figure 11-5. The easiest way to cut this cone is to use the rotary rasp and your drill. If using a drill press, leave the rotary rasp bit fully retracted in the press. Take the nozzle blank in your hand and hold it up to the rotary rasp bit. Grind off the water putty at a 45 degree angle, working from the throat hole on out. Rotate the nozzle in your hand as you cut and keep making the cone bigger and bigger. Try to make the cone as symmetrical as possible about the centerline of the throat.

Make sure that you don't get carried away and cut down past the throat and into the exit cone. The outer diameter of the entrance region cone should be no closer to the edge of the nozzle outer diameter than the inside chamber diameter. This does not mean that the entrance cone needs to extend to that point. The only purpose of the entrance region cone is to provide a smooth transition for the gases flowing down the chamber into the nozzle to minimize flow losses. Make the entrance cone outer diameter as large as necessary for this purpose, but no more.

If you are going to use a phenolic or graphite piece inside the water putty to reduce throat erosion, the nozzle is made the same way as if it was all water putty except for a few differences. First, it is better to drill out the phenolic or graphite insert before putting it into the water putty. This is particularly true for large throat diameters. The drill bit will often grab during the drilling process and if the insert is already imbedded into the water putty, this grabbing can cause the water putty to crack. Second, put the insert at the bottom of the water putty, Figure 11-6. If you put the insert on the end inside the chamber, the water putty downstream from the insert can failure during the motor burn

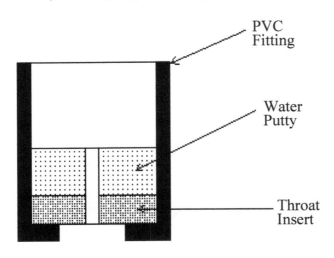

Figure 11-6: Graphite or Phenolic Insert at Bottom of PVC Fitting Filled With Water Putty

in ways that will cause the motor thrust to not be aligned with the motor axis.

Making Bulkheads

You have the option of using a delay charge in your bulkhead. My personal recommendation would be to skip the delay charge and use an altimeter/ejection or timer deployment system. The only exception to this would be with the small diameter motors, which usually go into small diameter rockets. In this case, put a delay charge in the bulkhead or end cap. PVC end caps make the easiest bulkheads, but you can also use solid plastic or metal. In either case, you can insulate the inside surface with a layer of RTV silicone rubber or rubber sheet. A thickness of insulation on the order of 3/32 inch will be adequate in most cases.

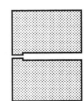

Figure 11-7: Solid Bulkhead with Delay Charge

If you are using a delay charge in a solid bulkhead, you will need to drill two holes for the delay charge. Drill a 1/2 inch diameter hole in the center of the bulkhead that is 0.25 inches short of going all the way through the bulkhead, Figure 11-7. It is not necessary that the hole be exactly in the center of the bulkhead. Now, drill a 3/32 inch hole in the same hole all the way through the bulkhead. Use a flat file to remove any burrs from drilling the holes.

PVC End Cap Bulkhead

If your motor does not have a delay charge, then simply insulate the end cap with a layer of RTV silicone rubber or bond in a piece of small rubber sheet. If you use an end cap with a delay charge, you can put it on the inside as shown in Figure 11-8. First, drill a hole in the center of the end cap about 3/32 inch in diameter. Then, cut a piece of 1/2 inch PVC pipe to the desired length of the delay charge. Glue the short 1/2 inch PVC pipe to the inside of the end cap using primer and PVC cement. Next, cut a piece of the 1/2 inch PVC pipe about 3/8 inches long. This little piece of pipe will eventually hold your ejection charge. Glue this piece to the outside of the PVC end cap using primer and PVC cement. After all this is done, make sure the 3/32 inch hole in the end cap has not become blocked by cement. If it has, redrill it.

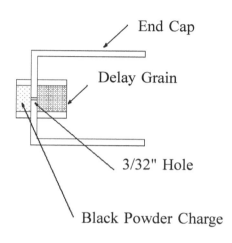

End Cap

Delay Grain

3/32" Hole

Black Powder Charge

Figure 11-8: PVC End With Delay Grain

A note of caution on your chamber length when using an end cap with a delay charge, you will have to make the chamber longer by the amount of delay length. Make sure you take this into account when cutting the chamber pipe to length.

How to Mix Propellant
Chapter 12

In Chapter 4, you learned how to determine the correct amounts for each propellant ingredient. In this chapter, we will go through the procedure for safely mixing a composite propellant. It is important to follow this sequence of mixing the propellant chemicals, particularly with respect to the powdered oxidizers and metals. Never mix dry oxidizers and powder metals together without a binder. An ignition source can turn that mixture into a flash of heat and flame that will result in severe burns, if you are close. This is true whether you are using ammonium nitrate or ammonium perchlorate as the oxidizer. In this chapter, we will go through the procedure for mixing an ammonium nitrate propellant. For ammonium perchlorate composite propellants, substitute ammonium perchlorate for ammonium nitrate and aluminum powder for magnesium powder. Of course the proportions will be different depending on what formulation you are making as referenced in Chapter 4.

It is also important to emphasize the need to make small propellant test batches when you are making a new formulation. These test batches should be about 50 grams in total weight and cast into a small disposable cup. Once the amount of curing agent has been adjusted so that the propellant has the desired properties, test batches are no longer necessary unless you change to a different curing agent or change the formulation.

Required Measuring and Mixing Equipment

Before mixing the propellant, it is important to have all the required equipment to measure the ingredients and mix them together. The first thing to get is a container to mix the propellant in. I recommend a Pyrex beaker for small batches of propellant. If you do not have a Pyrex beaker, a Pyrex measuring cup will work. You can buy these in the cooking section of any discount store. Don't use your wife's measuring cup, as she will give you hell, if you do. Make sure the cup or beakers you buy are large enough to hold your propellant batch.

When you buy your measuring cup, buy a package of plastic spoons used for picnics. Buy the more sturdy ones, if they are available. Also, buy a small metal spoon (teaspoon). You will also need a plastic or wooden stirring rod. The rod should be about 1/4 inch in diameter for sample propellant batches and 1/2 inch diameter for larger propellant batches. They should be long enough so that it goes into the beaker and you can grip it well enough to stir with it.

Another item you will need is more expensive. It is a balance for weighing all the ingredients. These are available from laboratory supply houses and sell for around $125. I recommend an open pan balance as shown in Figure 12-1. This type of balance can hold a large diameter bowel when you make large propellant batches with an electric mixer. The balance must be capable of measuring down to a tenth of a gram as you must measure your curing agent with this accuracy for small batches of propellant.

Figure 12-1: Propellant Mixing Equipment

If you are going to be making large batches of propellant, you will want to get an electric mixer, Figure 12-1. Mixing large batches of propellant (over 100 grams) by hand is not really feasible. I have used a Kitchen Aid Classic mixer with great success. They are available at Wal Mart, K-Mart and discount houses for $175 to $200. It will mix about one gallon of propellant. You can use electric "egg beater" type mixers, which are considerably cheaper. This type of mixer will chop the propellant mix as well as mix it, but the mixers can be found for only $40 on sale.

When you do use an electric mixer, it is important that you follow the procedures and steps in the same sequence as if you going to mix by hand. Mix the magnesium powder into the binder by hand. It is extremely important that the magnesium powder be mixed in by hand and completely wetted with binder before turning on the mixer.

NEVER PUT MAGNESIUM POWDER INTO THE BINDER IN AN ELECTRIC MIXING BOWL AND SIMPLY TURN ON THE MIXER. YOU CAN GET A MAGNESIUM DUST FIRE! ALWAYS STIR IN THE MAGNESIUM POWDER BY HAND SO THAT IT IS WETTED WITH BINDER FOLLOWING THE STEPS BELOW.

The ammonium nitrate oxidizer does not need to be stirred in by hand if using an electric mixer. It will not cause a dust fire or explosion.

List of Measuring and Mixing Equipment
Table 12-1

- Large Pyrex Beaker or Large Pyrex Measuring Cup
- Plastic or Wooden Stirring Rods - 1/4 inch Diameter to 1/2" inch Diameter
- Package of Plastic Spoons
- Metal spoon
- Balance Capable of Measuring in 10ths of a Gram
- Kitchen Aid Mixer or Electric Mixer

<u>Measuring and Mixing Ingredients</u>

By now you should have all your ingredients in hand and all the measuring and mixing equipment you will need. It's time to start making propellant. Again, it is extremely important to follow the sequence of mixing that is given in this book. Mixing out of this sequence can create a dangerous situation that could result in a metal dust fire, explosion or auto-ignition of the propellant. If you follow this sequence, the mixing will be absolutely safe. Needless to say, do not mix propellant near open flames or while smoking.

It is always good to mix propellant in a place where if it were to catch fire, it would not start anything else on fire. This could be outside or inside a very large open building. I would not mix propellant in the basement or garage. These places are too confined and a fire in there could burn down your entire house. Not a good prospect, especially if you are a renter. While the chances of the propellant catching fire are virtually zero, I believe it is better to be safe than sorry. Also, it is good to have a metal bucket of water next to you when mixing. If the propellant should ignite in the mixing bowel, simply drop the entire bowl with the burning propellant into it. That should extinguish it.

STEP 1: Set Up for Mixing

Before starting, always zero out your balance according to manufacturer`s directions. For mechanical balances, this is usually done with a thumbscrew so that the balance pointer will point to the zero mark. For electronic balances, you simply press the zero balance button.

Place your mixing bowl or cup on the balance plus your stirring rod. We are weighing the stirring rod since you will always have it in the mixing bowl during all subsequent measurements. Record the weight. (Example: Let's say the bowl and stirring rod weighs 100 grams.)

Add to the beaker/stirring rod weight, the weight of desired R45HT binder and record this as the Step #2 target weight. (Example: We want 25 grams of R45HT binder. Add 25 grams to 100 grams for a Step #2 target weight of 125 grams.)

Set the slides on your balance to125 grams. If using an electronic balance, simply record the target weight.

STEP 2: Adding the R45HT Binder

Open the container of R45HT binder. Use one of your plastic spoons and scoop out some of the binder. Its consistency will be like honey. Twirl the spoon around slowly to minimize the dripping of the binder off of the spoon. Hold the spoon over the bowl/stirring rod or cup/stirring rod and let the binder drip into bowl or cup.

If you are using a mechanical balance, watch the arm to see when it starts to lift off the rest. If using an electronic balance, watch the digital display as you get close to the Step #2 target weight. Regardless of balance, add the binder slowly so you will be able to stop adding binder when you reach the target weight. Depending on the amount of binder being added, you will probably have to dip your spoon several times into the binder bottle to get enough binder into your propellant bowl or cup.

Once the Step #2 target weight has been reached, stop adding binder. Close the binder bottle and throw away the plastic spoon.

STEP 3: Adding the Magnesium Powder

It is important to point out that up to this point, nothing you have been doing is dangerous. This is the step were you must observe caution. Magnesium or metal dust can be explosive and static electricity or a spark can ignite magnesium powder. When you add magnesium powder, pour it into the mixing bowl or cup as close to the top of the binder as you can. Make sure you do not have static electricity in your body. Touch a grounded object like a water pipe. I do not want to scare the pants off you, as magnesium powder will not do much of anything unless you form a dust cloud with it. That's what you have to watch out for, magnesium powder suspended in the air. So go carefully and don't start throwing powder all over place.

To the target weight from Step 2, add the desired weight of magnesium to equal the Step 3 target weight. (Example: Step 2 target weight was 125 grams and the desired weight of magnesium in our propellant is 20 grams. Then, our Step #3 target weight is 125 plus 20 to equal 145 grams.)

As in Step #2, set your slides on the mechanical balance for 145 grams. For the electronic balance, simply record the Step #3 target weight.

Now, carefully open the magnesium container. Do not shake the container before opening it. Using a spoon, carefully scoop out some of the magnesium powder. Slowly pour the magnesium powder from the spoon into the propellant mixing bowl/stirring rod or cup/stirring rod. Watch your balance so that you do not exceed your Step #3 target weight.

Make sure to put the spoon just a little bit above the binder inside the bowl or cup. This ensures that the distance the magnesium powder falls is minimal. By adding the magnesium in this manner, you will eliminate the potential for magnesium dust clouds. After adding the magnesium powder to the propellant mix, put the spoon down and close up the magnesium container. Remove the container from your mix station. Also, clean and put your metal spoon away.

NOW, TAKE YOUR STIRRING ROD AND SLOWLY MIX THE MAGNESIUM POWDER INTO THE BINDER. KEEP STIRRING UNTIL <u>ALL</u> OF THE MAGNESIUM POWDER IS COATED WITH BINDER. MAKE SURE THE MAGNESIUM POWDER ALONG THE SIDES OF THE BOWL IS COATED WITH BINDER.

You will be able to visually tell when the magnesium powder is coated as it will be a different shade of gray from dry magnesium powder. You will find that as more and more magnesium powder becomes coated that it will become harder and take longer to mix all the magnesium powder into the binder. Once the magnesium powder is completely covered with binder, it basically becomes inert so don't worry about it. It is just the uncoated magnesium you have to be careful with.

DO NOT PUT THE SAME SPOON USED FOR MAGNESIUM INTO THE AMMONIUM NITRATE BOTTLE OR SCOOP AMMONIUM NITRATE UP WITH IT! A MIXTURE OF DRY MAGNESIUM AND AMMONIUM NITRATE CAN AUTO-IGNITE IN THE PRESENCE OF MOISTURE.

Now, you are ready to move on to Step #4. But first, congratulate yourself because you have just completed the hardest and most hazardous step. Although, it really wasn't that dangerous.

STEP #4: Adding Ammonium Nitrate Oxidizer

To the target weight from Step 3, add the desired weight of ammonium nitrate to obtain the Step 4 target weight. (Example: Step 3 target weight was 145 grams and the desired weight of ammonium nitrate in our propellant is 55 grams. Then, our Step #4 target weight is 145 plus 55 to equal 200 grams.)

As in Step #3, set your slides on the mechanical balance for 200 grams. For the electronic balance, simply record the Step #4 target weight.

Open the ammonium nitrate container and using a plastic spoon scoop out ammonium nitrate powder. Pour the spoonful of ammonium nitrate into the bowl/stirring rod or cup/stirring rod containing the binder/magnesium mix. There is no need to worry about ammonium nitrate dust, so relax.   Keep adding ammonium nitrate powder until you reach your Step #4 target weight. Then close the bottle of ammonium nitrate powder and put it away.

Now, take your stirring rod and slowly mix the ammonium nitrate powder into the binder/magnesium mix. Keep stirring until all the ammonium nitrate powder is coated with binder. Remember to push the scrapings along the side of the bowl or cup down into your mixture. It may be hard to mix the ammonium nitrate into the propellant mix, but keep working it. It will eventually go in.

Take a look at your creation. It is uncured solid rocket propellant. All it needs now is the curing agent and it`s done.

STEP #5: Adding the Curing Agent

To the target weight from Step 4, add the desired weight of curing agent to equal the Step 5 target weight. (Example: Step 4 target weight was 200 grams and the desired weight of Mondur MR curing agent in our propellant is 2.3 grams. Then, our Step #5 target weight is 200 plus 2.3 to equal 202.3 grams.)

As in Step #4, set your slides on the mechanical balance for 202.3 grams. For the electronic balance, simply record the Step #5 target weight.

This is the last step and it is critical that you get just the right amount of curing agent into the propellant mix. The amount of curing agent is usually in terms of drops of fluid for sample propellant batches and a few spoonfuls for larger propellant batches.

Open the container of curing agent. Take a plastic spoon and pour out a small amount of liquid on the spoon. As best you can, add a little curing agent from the spoon to the propellant mix. Watch your balance, if you have reached the target weight, then stop adding curing agent. Add another small amount of curing agent, if you have not reached your Step #5 target weight. Continue this process until you reach your Step #5 target weight. Through away the spoon and close the container of curing agent.

Now, take your stirring rod and thoroughly mix the curing agent into the propellant mix, if you are mixing by hand. If you are using an electric mixer, put the bowl into the mixer and turn it on. The curing agent must be mixed throughout the propellant for it to properly cure. As you stir the mix, you will notice that it gets thinner and becomes more fluid. A couple of minutes of mixing should be sufficient for small hand mixes. For larger batches in an electric mixer, I would recommend about five to sevens minutes of mixing.

CONGRATULATIONS. YOU HAVE MADE A BATCH OF COMPOSITE SOLID ROCKET PROPELLANT! I'LL BET YOU DIDN'T THINK IT WAS THIS SIMPLE.

Adding Curing Agent After Adding The Binder

If you are going to make a batch of propellant that is really thick, you can add the curing agent after adding the binder to the bowl. This ensures that the curing agent is mixed uniformly throughout the binder. If you do this, add the magnesium powder after the curing agent and then the ammonium nitrate last.

However, a big word of caution here, once the curing agent is added to the mix, the clock starts running on the propellant curing. If you are using a fast curing agent, you may find the propellant is setting up on you before you can get it into your cartridges or chamber.

Casting the Propellant
Chapter 13

In the last chapter, you learned how to mix your propellant. You will only need a few simple things to be able to cast it into your motor. The items required are shown in Table 13-1.

Required Casting Equipment and Materials
Table 13-1

- Plastic or wooden rods from 1/4 inch on up to the propellant web thickness in diameter
- Plastic spoons
- Core rod
- Wax paper
- Silicone grease

The plastic or wooden rods are for smoothing out the free end of the propellant after it is cast. They are also used to tamp down the propellant as it is being cast to remove air bubbles. The diameter of the rod should be no smaller than 1/4 inch in diameter and can be as large as the propellant web thickness. However, the rod must be small enough to fit between the core and insulated motor chamber wall or cartridge wall in order to tamp the propellant down. It is best to keep the rod a little smaller than the web thickness so that it can move more freely between the walls and core rod.

For small diameter propellant cartridges with small cores, you will not use a core rod. In these cases, you will simply drill out the cured propellant to form a core. For the larger diameter cartridges or casting directly into the chamber, you will use a core rod. Make sure the rod is the same diameter desired for the core. Wrap the outside of the rod with wax paper and use tape to hold the wax paper in place.

Whether you are casting your propellant into a rubber lined chamber or phenolic sleeve, make sure the surface is clean of dust or dirt. Any dust particles will weaken the propellant bond to the rubber or phenolic sleeve walls.

A Simple Straight Core Casting Fixture

For some motors, you will be using a casting core inside the chamber, which will be removed when the propellant is cured. I recommend that you make a casting fixture, Figure 13-1. Essentially on a wood board, you mount a small piece of plastic rod about 3/4 inches long using flathead wood screws. Make sure the diameter of the rod matches or is just a little smaller than the inside diameter of the insulated chamber. In the center of the plastic rod, drill a hole for a small metal pin. The pin can be a small diameter nail that has been cut to a short length. Hammer the pin into the hole so that it sticks up about a 1/2 inch. In the center of the your casting rod, drill a hole with the same diameter of the pin that is a little over a 1/2 inch deep.

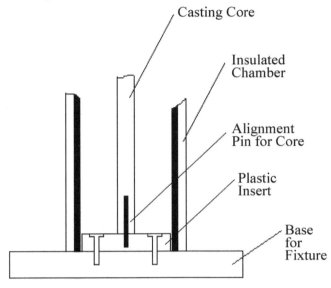

Figure 13-1: A Simple Casting Fixture

Casting the Straight Core Motor

The straight core fixture is used for this motor. First, apply silicone grease to the base of the fixture that will be inside the insulated rocket chamber. The insulated chamber is then slid onto the fixture. The fit should be sufficient to hold the insulated chamber upright. Then, the casting core is inserted into the insulated chamber. The core should be located so the hole in the core slides into the pin of the plastic rod. In this way the casting core is centered in the chamber.

Start adding propellant a spoonful at a time. Use a long wooden dowel that is smaller in diameter than the propellant web thickness to work the propellant down to the bottom of the chamber. If the propellant is pourable, then pour a small amount in at first. Keep adding small amounts of propellant at a time and working it to the bottom of the chamber. It is important that you fill all gaps to minimize voids in the propellant. When the chamber has been filled to the proper level, make sure the casting core is centered in the motor.

Casting the End Burner

Tape one end of the rocket chamber with duct tape. Fill the open end of the chamber with propellant using the same procedures as for the straight core. Make sure you do a good job in tapping the propellant down to the bottom.

Casting Propellant cartridges

For cartridges where you are going to drill out the core, simply put a piece of duct tape over one end of the cartridge. If you are going to drill out the core, fill the cartridge with propellant using the same procedures as for the straight core. If the core in the propellant cartridge is too big to be drilled or the propellant cartridge is too long, center the core rod in the cartridge and press down on it so that it sticks to the duct tape sealing one end of the cartridge. Fill the gap around the core with propellant until you reach the top of the cartridge. As before, put a little propellant in at a time and work it down to the bottom. Use the same procedures as for the straight core when adding the propellant.

Casting The Moon Burner

Follow the same directions as for the straight core burner except remove the centering pin from the fixture. When the propellant is poured into the sleeve, place the casting core off from the center. If the position of the moon core is important, a new pin location can be drilled into the plastic rod or a new casting fixture can be made.

Casting The C Slot Burner

Use the same fixture as the straight core without the centering pin. Obtain a Teflon bar that is the same dimensions as the slot. Liberally coat the outside of the bar with silicone grease. Place this greased bar into the open end of the insulated chamber against one of the walls. It's ok that silicone grease will get on the wall where the bar is against it. Just make sure you do not get silicone grease on the other sleeve walls where propellant will be located. The chamber is now ready for casting. Add small amounts of propellant and keep the bar against the chamber wall. As you get more propellant into the chamber, the bar will be held in place by the propellant. As with the other patterns, make sure you work the propellant in the chamber to minimize voids.

Casting The Delay Charge

If you are using a delay charge in your motor, you can cast it at the same time you are casting your motor chamber or filling propellant cartridges. For the delay tube cemented to the PVC end cap type, you just fill the tube with propellant, Figure 13-2. As it is a little bigger in diameter, it is also easier to fill with propellant. However, it is still important to force the propellant in and work out any air bubbles.

For the solid bulkhead delay charge, fill the delay hole with propellant to the depth required for the proper delay. Make sure you really force the propellant into it so that there will be no gaps in the delay charge.

To clean up your mixing and casting tools when done, use Simple Green concentrate cleaning fluid. Do not dilute it with water, but use it straight out of the concentrate bottle. It will easily remove propellant from the blades, tools and your fingers and hand.

<u>Curing</u>

After you have added all the propellant to the chamber or propellant cartridge, place it in a location where the room temperature is not below 75° F. It must be oriented vertically with the open end up. Depending on room temperature and curing agent, it will take a few hours to about 48 hours for the propellant to completely cure. With the Mondur MR, the propellant should be hard enough that it will hold a shape within four hours. If you push your finger on it, it should return to the original shape. You can check the propellant for a complete cure by seeing if it is still tacky or soft. If it is, then the propellant has not fully cured yet.

Figure 13-2: End Cap Delay Charge with Propellant

After the propellant has cured, you are ready to remove the casting tools. If you used the straight core casting fixture, remove the base of the casting fixture from the chamber, first. You can just twist and pull it out. Remove the casting rod in the motor next by giving it a sharp twist and pulling. You may have to do this a couple of times before it lets go. After it releases, pull the rod out slowly. If you have a rectangular bar from the c-slot pattern, twist it a little and then pull it out.

If you used wax paper to cover the core rod, you will find the paper stuck to the inside of the core. You can clean some of it out by using a screwdriver and prying it out. The remainder can be cleaned out with coarse sandpaper glued on the end of a rod. Slowly run the rod up and down the core to clean out the paper. It is not necessary to get all of the wax paper out, as it will burn out almost immediately when the motor ignites.

If you are drilling out the core, drill at a slow speed and remove the drill bit often from the core to get out propellant shavings. Put the shavings into a cup away from your workstation as you drill out the propellant cartridges. When you are done drilling all of your cartridges, you can burn off the shavings or save them for use in making igniters.

<u>Trimming the Propellant</u>

After the propellant cures, it will swell up a little and expand out of the open end of the chamber, cartridge and delay charge tube, Figure 13-3. Trim the excess propellant with a sharp

Figure 13-3: Propellant Has
Swelled in Chamber After
Curing

kitchen knife.   For the chamber or cartridge, trim the propellant so that it does not interfere with the bulkhead, end cap or nozzle.   Any thin pieces of propellant hanging from bores or slots can be trimmed with a sharp knife.   This is not really necessary, but it does make the propellant grain look more professional.

Final Assembly
Chapter 14

You've made all the parts and cast the motor. Now, you are ready to put all the parts together and finish your motor.   The procedures in this chapter are oriented towards the PVC pipe motors, but this same basic approach would apply if you were using other materials.

1 Inch PVC Pipe Motor

The first step is to coat the inside of the end cap with a layer of RTV rubber, Figure 14-1. The layer should be approximately 1/16 inch thick. If your end cap has a delay charge, you can skip coating the inside of the end with RTV rubber.   If your end cap does not have a delay charge, coat the inside flange of the end cap with primer.   Coat the outside of one end of the PVC chamber with primer.   Put a layer of PVC cement on the inside flange of the end cap and outside of the end of the PVC pipe. These will be the same surfaces you put the primer on. If your end cap has a delay charge, do not put PVC cement on the inside flange of the end cap. Stick the end cap onto the end of the PVC pipe coated with cement. Let it dry for about one hour before going on to the next step.

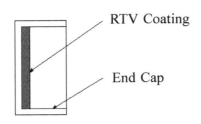

Figure 14-1: RTV Coating Inside 1" PVC End Cap

Load the propellant cartridges into the PVC pipe chamber.   After the last cartridge is in the chamber, it should come just to the end of the chamber.   Put a thin layer of RTV rubber on the inside surface of the water putty nozzle.   The thickness should be about 1/16 inch.   Coat the inside surface of the nozzle flange and outside end of the PVC pipe with primer.   Then, coat these same surfaces with PVC cement.   Push the nozzle all the way onto the PVC pipe chamber.   Let the motor stand for 24 hours at room temperature in a horizontal position so that the PVC cement can completely set.   When the 24 hours is up, your motor is ready for firing.

2.0 to 4.0 Inch PVC Pipe Motors

The first step is to put a 1/16 inch thick piece of rubber sheet inside the end cap.   The rubber inserted inside the cap should cover the entire inside of the cap unless you have a delay grain inside the cap. In that case, cut a circle in the rubber so that the delay grain is exposed when the rubber insulation is put into the end cap.   Usually there will be small gaps around the edges no matter how careful you cut it.   Fill these gaps with high temperature RTV silicone

Figure 14-2: RTV Coating on Chamber where End Cap Goes

rubber. Put dabs on a screwdriver and work it into the gaps. Also, put a thin layer of RTV silicone rubber on the PVC chamber end ridge and internal insulation ridge where the end cap will go, Figure 14-2.

Coat the outside end of the PVC chamber and the inside surface of the end cap that will make contact with the chamber with PVC primer. Coat these same surfaces with PVC cement. Push the end cap all the way onto the PVC chamber.

Now, do the same thing with the PVC fitting nozzle. Put a layer of RTV silicone rubber around the inside edge of the nozzle fitting and on the PVC chamber end ridge. Coat the outside of the PVC pipe with primer along with the inside of the fitting. Then, coat these same surfaces with PVC cement and push the nozzle fitting onto the PVC pipe.

Let the motor assembly stand with the nozzle up for 24 hours at room temperature so that all the PVC cement will completely set. After the 24 hours, your motor is ready to fire.

Bonding Retaining Pins Directly Into Nozzles And Bulkheads

As mentioned in Chapter 7, you may want to use retaining pins to help hold the bulkhead and nozzle into the chamber. After bonding the nozzle and bulkhead into place, let the adhesive used completely set before adding the retaining pins. Mark the end of the chamber circumferentially for the number of pins that will be evenly spaced around the chamber. These marks will be the locations for drilling the retaining pin holes. Start drilling the holes one by one making sure the hole diameters are just slightly larger than the retaining pin diameter. Drill the holes through the chamber into the nozzle or bulkhead to a depth that is halfway from the outer diameter of the nozzle to the throat diameter. If you are using a drill press with a calibrated drill depth, use that as a guide to drill the hole. If you are using a hand drill or a drill press that is not calibrated, put a ring of electrical tape around the drill bit at the point where the drill bit must stop.

Cut the retaining pins for the nozzle and bulkhead. Put a small amount of epoxy in each pin hole and insert the retaining pins. Push each pin into the hole as far as it will go. The top of the pin should be flush with the outside of the chamber. Wait for the epoxy to fully cure before doing anything else with the motor. After this time period, your examination of the motor may show some of the pins sticking out too far. You can use a flat file to file them down flush with the outer surface of the chamber, if you desire. Usually, if you have cut the pins carefully, filing is not necessary. Be careful in your filing so that you do not heat up the pin.

Bulkheads with Delay Charges

Some of your motors may use a delay charge. If you are using a solid bulkhead, it will be inserted inside the chamber. Coat the end of the bulkhead that will go inside the chamber with a 1/8 inch thick layer of RTV silicone rubber, Figure 14-3. Make sure you do not cover the delay charge. Run a bead of RTV silicone rubber where bulkhead face ends inside the chamber wall. When the bulkhead is inserted, it will push against this bead of RTV and form a seal.

Adding An Ejection Charge

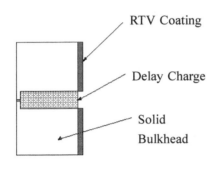

Figure 14-3: RTV Coating on Solid Bulkhead with Delay Charge

The final step is adding the ejection charge. Add the amount of charge based on the formula given in Chapter 18 on recovery systems.

Before you add the charge, make sure the hole in the bulkhead between the charge and delay propellant is clear and open. Take a small drill bit and clean out the hole. Watch out for static electricity during the process of adding the charge. Make sure you are grounded out. It is important that the black powder charge be in contact with the delay propellant. As you add the powder, make sure the powder is going into the small hole by shaking the motor.

After the charge is added, you must seal off the end of the tube holding the charge so that the powder stays in contact with the delay propellant. You do not want the charge to move out of the hole when the motor is turned horizontal or upside down. If the charge does not come to the end of the tube, fill the gap with cotton balls. Then, seal the end of the tube with masking tape. Use a couple of pieces so that the end is sealed off.

Static Testing Your Motor
Chapter 15

It is a good idea to static test your first motor and any new designs. It is better for the motor to explode on the test stand rather than in flight. The instructions provided in this book are as complete as possible, but it is hard to convey in words and pictures some of the subtleties of making a motor. This is why we recommend you static test your first "home made" rocket motor and new designs. In most cases, your motor will work fine and you will be ready to start producing motors.

It is important to remember that a successful static test firing only proves that the motor tested works. There will always be a small degree of uncertainty with an unfired motor of the same design. The degree of uncertainty is directly dependent on how carefully you make your motor. You must be consistent in making your motors. You must be consistent in your materials, insulators, adhesives and how you use them in making the motor. This is quality control. It is up to you to maintain quality in producing your motors.

Basic Static Testing

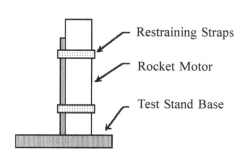

Figure 15-1: Simple Nozzle Up Static Firing Setup

Restraining Straps

Rocket Motor

Test Stand Base

Basic static testing is simply igniting the motor on a test stand to see if it works or fails. A basic fixture for holding the motor during this type of test is shown in Figure 15-1. The motor fires with the nozzle up so that the thrust of the motor is directed into the ground. The stand can be made of wood or metal, but if it is made of wood, make sure the vertical wood support does not extend above the nozzle. Otherwise, the exhaust plume of the motor will set the wood on fire. Anchor the base of the stand with cement blocks or any other heavy object so that the stand cannot tip over. The motor can be attached to the vertical support with metal straps or heavy gauge wire. You can fire the motor using the same electrical equipment that launches your rockets.

If you have a video camcorder, make a video of your static test. This will give you a record of the burn time and delay charge time, if you are using a delay charge. Put the camcorder on a tripod about 75 feet away from the motor to protect it from flying pieces should the motor explode. If your motor fails, you can examine your video one frame at a time on your VCR to see what went wrong. Your camcorder will take 30 frames a second, which is usually fast enough to spot the problem.

It is also a good idea to cut the motor open with a saw after the test firing. It is relatively easy to cut the PVC pipe chamber. Pull off the nozzle and bulkhead sections and examine them for excessive insulation erosion. If the insulation is very thin or you are melting into the plastic parts, then you should increase the insulation thickness or reduce the motor burn time.

Getting Burn Rate vs. Pressure Data

The best way to get burn rate versus pressure data is with pressure transducer measuring chamber pressure directly. However, you may not have the budget for that. Even with a simple static firing, you can get a good estimate of the average burn rate and related it to the chamber pressure. You can calculate the average burn rate for the motor by dividing the propellant web thickness by the burn time. If the web thickness is 0.565 and the burn time was 5 seconds, then the average burn rate was 0.71 inches/second (0.565/8 = 0.071).

Average Burn Rate = (Web Thickness) / (Burn Time)

Average Burn Rate = 0.565 / 5.0 = 0.113 Inches/second

The next thing to do is to estimate the chamber pressure. Recall from Chapter 1:

Chamber Pressure = (Propellant Weight Flowrate) * (C*) / [(Throat Area) *32.2]

We can use average values for the propellant weight flowrate and throat area to get an average chamber pressure. Let's say that the initial throat diameter was 0.375 inch and the final throat diameter was 0.423 inches. Then the average throat diameter was 0.399 inches ([0.375+0.423]/2 = 0.399). The average throat area was then:

Throat Area = (3.14/4) * (Throat Diameter)^2 = (0.785) * (0.399)^2 = 0.785 * 0.159

Throat Area = 0.125 inch^2

The value for C* is obtained from CHEM. As mentioned in Chapter 1, C* doesn't change very much with pressure. However, the C-star from CHEM is a theoretical value. From experience with small motors, it is reasonable to expect that the actual C* value may be about

0.90 time the CHEM predicted values. This is due to combustion inefficiencies. As an initial estimate, we will use 4162 ft/second.

The final parameter we need is the propellant flowrate. Suppose our motor had 2 lbs of propellant. Then, the propellant weight flowrate is the propellant weight divided by the burn time or 2 lbs divided by 5 seconds to yield 0.4 lbs/seconds. The average chamber pressure was then:

$$\text{Chamber Pressure} = (0.4 * 4162) / (0.125 * 32.2) = 1664.8/4.025 = 414 \text{ psi}$$

We can use this information to refine our burn rate data for this propellant formulation by plotting the average burn rate vs. average chamber pressure. Our one data point would be 0.113 inches/second at 414 psi. With each motor firing of a different motor and the same propellant formulation, you can determine the burning rate equation parameters or refine them. The more data points, the better your estimate of the burn rate parameters.

Measuring Chamber Pressure During A Static Test

The static test stand for measuring chamber pressure is a slight variation of the simple static test stand in Figure 15-1. The difference is that space must be made for the pressure line running from the bulkhead to the pressure transducer. This static test stand has a slight standoff so that the pressure line can come out of the bulkhead and make a turn off to the side, Figure 15-2. You can use 1/4 inch stainless steel tubing for the pressure line. This can be found at steel tubing supply houses or sometimes at surplus metal dealers. Cut the tubing to the required length, about 1.5 to two feet, using a metal hacksaw or tube cutter.

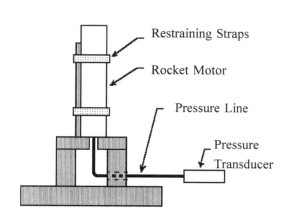

Figure 15-2: Nozzle Up Static Test Stand with Provision for Chamber Pressure Transducer

Your motor's end cap or bulkhead must be changed so that it will accept a pressure line. Buy a tap to thread a hole for a 1/8 inch NPT male fitting. Drill a hole in the center of the end cap or bulkhead to tap for a 1/8 inch NPT fitting. The hole diameter required for the tap will be provided with the tap. These taps can be bought at hardware stores. Buy a 1/8 inch

NPT brass or steel male fitting that accepts 1/4 inch tubing on the compression end. These can be found in hardware stores. Cover the threads of the fitting with Teflon tape and screw it into end cap of the motor.

Bend the 1/4 inch stainless steel tube 90 degrees. Be careful not to kink the tube. Connect one end of the tube to the fitting in the bulkhead or end cap and the other to the pressure transducer. The pressure transducer should have a pressure range to cover the expected chamber pressure. It is easier to get the data from the transducer if it has a 5 volt output. Omega Engineering carries pressure transducers for under $200 that can do the job. You will need a DC power supply for the transducer and twisted wire to connect up the transducer.

The output from the transducer can be recorded on your computer using a data acquisition plug-in module. These modules connect to your computer's RS-232 port and sell for around $100 including software. These units are very handy since they can be used in the field with a laptop computer. The modules are available from DATAQ. A specification sheet is usually provided with the transducer, which is useful for converting voltage output to pressure. It is usually a linear relationship. The transducer puts out one volt DC at zero pressure and five volts DC at maximum pressure. If the maximum pressure reading for the pressure transducer is 500 psi, then the relationship between voltage and pressure is as follows:

Pressure to voltage = (500 psi)/(4 volts) = 125 psi/volt above one volt

If the voltage output is 2.5 volts, we can convert that to pressure by first subtracting one volt off from the reading. Remember, you get one volt with no pressure at all. So, now we have a voltage of 1.5 volts. Multiply 1.5 volts by the pressure to voltage relationship to obtain the chamber pressure:

Chamber pressure = (1.5 volts) * (125 psi/volts) = 187.5 psi

One of the nice things about the DATAQ software package that comes with the module is that it will convert the voltage to pressure for you. You just input the upper and lower reference points for the pressure transducer such as 1 volt equal zero psi and five volts equal 1000 psi.

After you get your data from a test firing, you can use the DATAQ software to find the maximum pressure and the average or median pressure. Simply mark the start and end points of the pressure trace and press "Control T". The median pressure can be used as the average pressure in plotting up chamber pressure versus burn rate. The average burn rate is calculated as shown in the previous section.

You can also use the pressure data to estimate the actual delivered C* of the motor using the following equation:

$$C* \text{ (Delivered)} = [(\text{Average chamber pressure}) * (\text{Average throat area}) * (32.2)] / (\text{Average propellant weight flow rate})$$

The average chamber pressure you can get from the pressure-time data. If you are using DATAQ software, you can get it directly from that. The propellant weight flow rate is the weight of propellant divided by the burn time. The throat area is:

$$\text{Throat area} = (3.14/4) * (\text{Average throat diameter})^2$$

$$\text{Average throat diameter} = [(\text{Initial throat diameter}) + (\text{Final throat diameter})] / 2.0$$

The average propellant weight flow rate is the propellant weight divided by the burn time.

$$\text{Average propellant weight flow rate} = (\text{Propellant weight}) / (\text{Burn time})$$

Let`s take an example to show you how you do this. Suppose we have the following conditions for our motor firing:

- Propellant weight = 0.25 lbs
- Burn time = 3 seconds
- Average chamber pressure = 178 psi
- Initial throat diameter = 0.25 inches
- Final throat diameter = 0.325 inches
- Exit cone diameter = 0.50 inches
- C* prediction by CHEM = 4664 ft/second

Then:

$$\text{Average throat diameter} = [(0.25) + (0.325)] / 2 = 0.575/2 = 0.2875 \text{ inches}$$

$$\text{Average throat area} = (3.14/4) * (\text{Average throat diameter})^2 = 0.785 * (0.2875)^2$$

$$\text{Average throat area} = 0.0649 \text{ inches}^2$$

Average propellant weight flow rate = (0.25) / (3) = 0.083 lbs/second

C* (Delivered) = (178 * 0.0649 *32.2) / (0.083) = 371.98 / 0.083 = 4482 ft/second

We can get the c-star combustion efficiency using the following equation:

C* combustion efficiency = [(C-star theoretical from CHEM)/(C-star delivered)] * 100

C* combustion efficiency = (4482/4664) * 100 = 0.961 * 100 = 96.1 %

Converting Chamber Pressure to Thrust

We can make a very good estimate of the delivered thrust of the motor from the pressure data if the throat does not erode. The first thing to do is to determine the thrust coefficient of the motor. You do this by calculating the expansion ratio of the motor and then looking up the corresponding thrust coefficient in Appendix H. You use the following equation to convert chamber pressure to thrust:

Thrust = (Chamber pressure) * (Throat area) * (Nozzle coefficient)

If the throat erodes during the motor firing, the process of calculating the thrust is more complicated as the throat area and nozzle coefficient are no longer a constant. You can calculate the thrust using the following equation:

Thrust vs. Time = (Throat Area vs. Time) * (Pressure vs. Time) * (Nozzle coefficient vs. Time)

Measure the throat diameter after the firing and assume the throat diameter increased linearly with time from the initial throat diameter to the final diameter. This will allow you to calculate the throat area as a function of time.

Throat Diameter vs. Time = Initial Diameter + (Time) * [(Final Throat Diameter - Initial Throat Diameter)/(Total Burn Time)]

Throat Area = (3.14/4) * (Throat Diameter at given time)^2

Measure Thrust During A Static Firing

The best way is to directly measure the thrust using a load cell and a single axis thrust stand. The easiest way to use the load cell is with the nozzle end of the motor pointing up. Use the same basic design as shown in Figure 15-2, but mount the stand plate on a cantilever load cell, Figure 15-3. The load cell will have to be mounted to a base that does not move for accurate measurements. This base can be a small concrete slab or large metal plate that is well anchored to the ground.

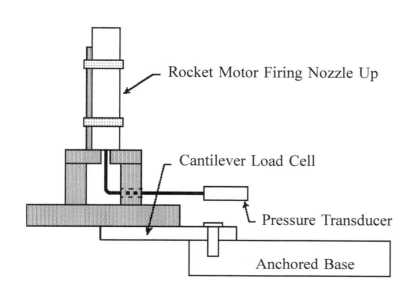

Figure 15-3: Test Stand For Measuring Thrust and Chamber Pressure

The load cell will require a supply voltage usually around 12 volts DC. Most load cells also have a very low voltage output that is in the millivolt range. This voltage must be amplified before being transmitted along lines to your computer. A signal amplifier using an INA 125 instrumentation amplifier microchip can be built based on the schematic shown in Figure 15-4. You adjust the variable resistor to get the desired voltage amplification. I would recommend amplifying the load cell signal so that a full-scale load on the cell produces 5 volts.

The lowest cost DATAQ module accepts two different inputs so you can input the chamber pressure and thrust of the motor. With measured thrust and chamber pressure data, you can completely characterize the motor. If the throat is non-eroding, you can make a good estimate of the chamber pressure using the following equation:

Chamber pressure = (Thrust) / [(Throat area) * (Nozzle coefficient)

The throat area and nozzle coefficient are calculated as shown in the previous section. From the calculate chamber pressure, you can estimate the C* combustion efficiency using the same procedures shown earlier.

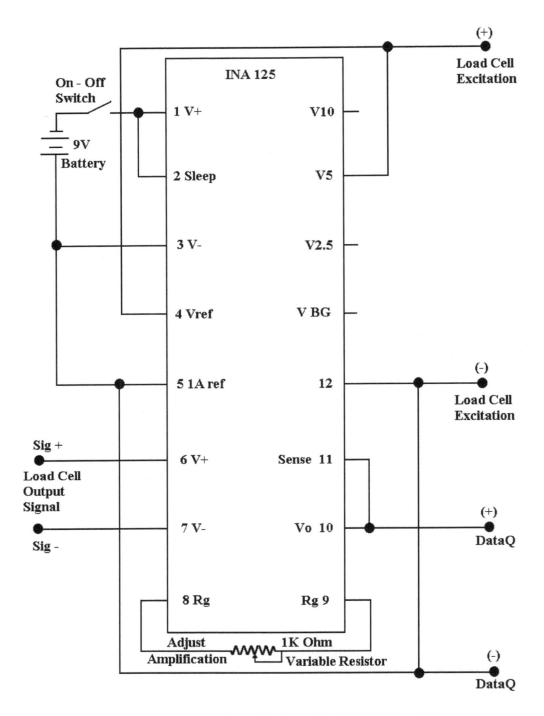

Figure 15-4: Schematic for a Load Cell Amplifier

Making the Rocket Body
Chapter 16

It's time to design the rocket and explore various methods of building it. The first thing to do after you know your motor's thrust-time curve is to run FLIGHT with the best estimate of the weight of the rocket. For our example, lets take a rocket that is 7.67 inches in diameter with an estimated empty weight of 15 lbs. The motor weights 3.13 lbs and contains 2.19 lbs of propellant. The thrust is initially 54.6 lbs and then ramps up to 103.3 lbs at 5.7 seconds, which is end of firing. Our estimate of the drag coefficient is 0.40. Running FLIGHT shows the maximum compressive force on the body tube is 36.8 lbs at 5.7 seconds into the flight, Figure 16-1.

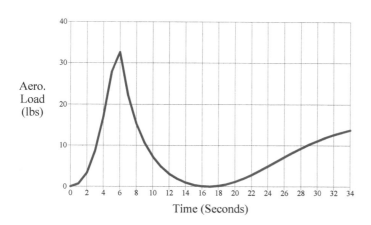

Figure 16-1: Compressive Force on an Amateur Rocket

For body tubes, the choice of materials is usually fiberboard, phenolic, fiberglass, PVC and aluminum. The choice of material usually depends on whether it can survive the aerodynamic loads of the flight and cost. In our case, the aerodynamic loads are relatively low at 37 lbs. Fiberboard should give us an acceptable margin. To illustrate, how you would calculate the maximum load for your body tube, let's do a sample calculation.

Body tubes under aerodynamic compression load can be grouped into three classes based on the slenderness ratio. The slenderness ratio is defined as:

Slenderness Ratio = SL = (Body Tube Length) / (Body Tube Radius of Gyration)

Body Tube Radius of Gyration = Square Root[{(Outer Diameter)^2 + (Inner Diameter)^2}/8]

The three groups of body tube situations are (1) compression blocks (SL less than 30), (2) short columns (SL = 30 to 120) and (3) long columns (SL above 60) For typical amateur rockets, the slenderness ratio is going be fall in the categories of either compression blocks or short columns. So, the first thing to do is to find out which category your body tube falls into by calculating the slenderness ratio. Our body tube has an outside diameter of 7.67 inches with an inside diameter of 7.52 inches and is 60 inches long. The radius of gyration is:

Radius of gyration = Square root[{$(7.67)^2 + (7.52)^2$}/8] = Square root[(58.83 + 56.55)/8]

Radius of gyration = Square root[115.38/8] = Square root[57.69] = 3.80 inches

Slenderness Ratio = 60/3.80 = 15.8

For this slenderness ratio, we fall in the category of a short block, because the ratio is less then 30.

Compression Block Type Body Tubes (SL <30)

For this case, the failure load or maximum aerodynamic load the body tube can experience before damage is calculated by the following expression:

Failure Load = 0.785 * (Allowable Compressive Strength) * ($D^2_{Outer} - D^2_{Inner}$)

In order to make this calculation, you need to know the allowable compressive strength of your body tube material. The allowable compressive strength will usually be far less than the ultimate compressive strength. Allowable means no permanent damage is done to the tube, while ultimate mean catastrophic failure. The allowable compressive strengths for different materials are listed Table 16-1. Please note that at the printing of this edition, some of the values had to be estimated based on what was recorded in technical literature and from experience.

Allowable Compressive Strengths For Some Rocket Body Materials
Table 16-1

Material	Allowable Compressive Strength (psi)
Fiberboard	5,000 (Estimate)
PVC	9,600
Phenolic XX	34,000
Phenolic CE	39,000
Epoxy laminate G-10	68,000
Aluminum	34,500

16-2

For our sample case, the aerodynamic failure load that would damage our body tube is:

$$\text{Failure Load} = 0.785 * 5000 * [(7.67)^2 - (7.52)^2] = 0.785 * 5000 * (58.83 - 56.55)$$

$$\text{Failure Load} = 0.785 * 5000 * 2.28 = 8949 \text{ lbs}$$

Now this may seem like a lot of load for a fiberboard tube, but when the tube is short and in compression, it does have a lot of strength. If you are not convinced, take a short piece of tube and stand on it. Put your weight on it gently and evenly. You will be amazed at how much weight you can put on it.

Again, this formula assumes that the load is gently placed on the tube and distributed evenly around the tube. If the load is not distributed evenly, than the failure load is reduced:

$$\text{Offset Failure Load} = \text{Failure Load When Symmetric} / (1+\{[8 * e]/\text{Diameter}\})$$

$$e = \text{Offset of the load from center}$$

Let's take the above example and say the load is offset 2 inches from center. Then the maximum load is reduced to:

$$\text{Failure Load} = 8949 /(1 + \{[8 * 2] / 7.67\}) = 8949 / (1+\{16/7.67\}) = 8949 /(1+2.09)$$
$$\text{Failure Load} = 8949/3.09 = 2896 \text{ lbs}$$

For our rocket, we are in good shape as the body tube should be able to handle the aerodynamic loads, even if off center. To illustrate the calculation if your rocket is long and slender, let's suppose your body tube falls into the short column category.

Short Columns (SL between 30 and 120)

We have a body tube of fiberboard which has an outside diameter of 7.67 inches, an inside diameter of 7.52 inches and is 12 ft or 144 inches long. Recalling that the radius of gyration was 3.80 inches, the slenderness ratio would be as follows:

$$\text{Slenderness Ratio} = 144/3.80 = 37.9$$

There are not exact equations for this type of column, so over the years empirical expressions have been developed that are dependent on the material. The expression for aluminum is well established, but those for fiberboard, phenolic and PVC has been estimated for this book.

$$\underline{\text{Aluminum:}} \text{ Failure Load} = 0.785 * (d^2_{outer} - d^2_{inner}) * (34500 - [173.2 * SL])$$

$$\underline{\text{Fiberboard:}} \text{ Failure Load} = 0.785 * (d^2_{outer} - d^2_{inner}) * (5000 - [1.67 * SL])$$

$$\underline{\text{Phenolic XX:}} \text{ Failure Load} = 0.785 * (d^2_{outer} - d^2_{inner}) * (34000 - [2.5 * SL])$$

$$\underline{\text{PVC:}} \text{ Failure Load} = 0.785 * (d^2_{outer} - d^2_{inner}) * (9600 - [4.16 * SL])$$

Using the expression for fiberboard, we then calculate the maximum allowable compressive load on the body tube:

$$\text{Failure Load} = 0.785 * ([7.67]^2 - [7.52]^2) * [5000 - (1.67 * 37.9)]$$

$$\text{Failure Load} = 0.785 * (58.83 - 56.55) * [5000 - 63.3] = 0.785 * 2.28 * 4936.7$$

$$\text{Failure Load} = 8836 \text{ lbs}$$

As you can see, as the failure load went down from 8,949 lbs to 8,836 lbs by simply making the body tube longer. Still, this is plenty of strength for our rocket body tube. Typically, rockets fail not with a collapse of the body tube, but with a failure of the coupler or the fins.

Couplers

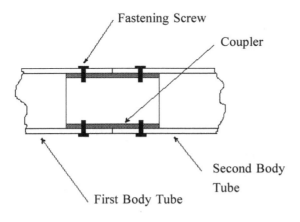

Figure 16-2: Coupler Connecting Two Body Tubes

Body tubes come in stock lengths of three or four feet. For longer rockets, you need to connect the body tubes together. This is done with couplers, which are short pieces of tubing that slide inside the body tube. One end of the coupler tube is fastened to one end of a body tube and the other is fastened to the other body tube, Figure 16-2. The coupler can be permanently bonded to both pieces of body tube, but usually it is attached with screws so

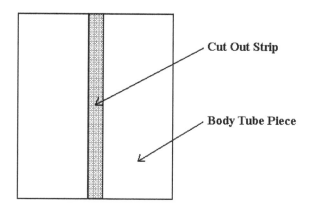

Cut Out Strip

Body Tube Piece

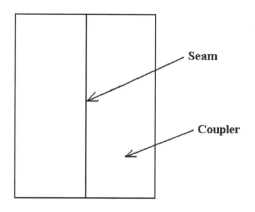

Seam

Coupler

Figure 16-3: Making a Coupler Out of a Piece of Body Tube

that the rocket can be taken apart. This is handy for transportation and for placing electronic packages inside the rocket. When you fasten the coupler into the body tube, make sure you really fasten it securely, as in flight; the rocket will try to bend at the coupler joint. To help provide structural support at the coupler, each end of the coupler should go into the rocket tube about one body tube diameter. So, for our case each end of the coupler should go into the body tube about 7.67 inches.

Often it is hard to find a tube that will slip exactly inside the body tube. This is particularly true if your body tube is non-standard in size. An easy way to make a coupler is to cut an extra piece from the body tube material to the desired length of your coupler. Then, cut a piece out of it in the axial direction so that when the ends of the cut piece are butted together, it slides inside the body tube, Figure 16-3. You can glue the ends together or you can glue the axial strip you cut out to the inside wall of the coupler at the joint.

Fins

You can make your fins out of PVC, phenolic, composites or aircraft quality wood. In selecting your fin material, you must make sure it is strong not to bend easily for your fin size. This is very important. If the fin can flex after it is mounted to the rocket, it will do so in flight. This will cause the rocket to start wobbling and cause it to experience sudden, large angles of attack. If this condition is severe enough, the fins will break off from the rocket body. In some cases, the fins may stay attached, but the fins themselves will break.

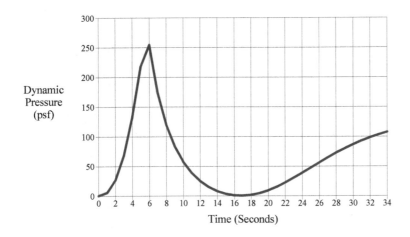

Figure 16-4: Dynamic Pressure on an Amateur Rocket

It is important that you attach your fins securely to the rocket body. For small rockets with relatively small fins, you can often bond the fins to the body with adhesive. You can use epoxy cement or if you are using PVC fins, you can glue them on with PVC cement and PVC angle brackets. It is important to note that this bonding approach is good if the fins are relatively small and the rocket speeds are not great. A good rule of thumb is if you can break them off by hand, then they are probably not fastened onto the rocket body strong enough.

A better way to fasten the fins onto the rocket body is to use aluminum angle bracket with bolts and nuts. You can buy long strips of aluminum angle stock in different sizes from hardware and home improvement stores. Cut the aluminum so that it runs almost the length of the fin where it attaches to the rocket body. Make sure you use washers where the bolts go through the fins and rocket body.

You can make an estimate of the maximum aerodynamic force on your fins by first looking at the maximum dynamic pressure your rocket experiences. From FLIGHT, we see for our example, that the maximum dynamic pressure is approximately 250 lbs per square foot, Figure 16-4. If your rocket should turn 90 degrees and was suddenly flying sideways, a fin one square foot in size would experience a 250 lb force trying to break it off. Of course, you rockets should not be flying sideways. When they are flying in the direction of travel this pressure is exerted on the leading edge of the fin. The force on the fin under that condition is:

Fin force @ 0 angle of attack = [(Dynamic pressure) * (Fin thickness) * (Fin base)] / 144.

Let`s say our fin is 1/8 inch thick and the distance it sticks out from the rocket body is 10 inches, then.

Fin force @ 0 angle of attack = [(250) * (0.125) * (10.)] / 144. = 312.5 / 144. = 2.2 lbs

16-6

That is not very much force. Let`s take a look at the force on the fin, if the rocket turns 90 degrees and starts flying sideways.

Fin force @ 90 angle of attack = [(Dynamic pressure) * (Fin root) * (Fin base)] / 144.

In our case, we will make the length of fin attached to the rocket root seven inches. Then:

Fin force @ 90 angle of attack = [(250) * (7) * (10)] / 144. = 17500 / 144 = 122 lbs

That amount of force is not insignificant and it would break many adhesive bonds used to hold fins on. Now, that is obviously a worse case and our rocket should not turn sideways in flight. However, if the fins are a little flexible, the rocket may start to turn slightly away from the direction of travel. Let`s call this angle of attack "α". Then,

Fin force @ α angle of attack = [cosine (α) * (Fin force @ 0 angle of attack)] + [sine (α) * (Fin force @ 90 angle of attack)]

Suppose we look at a five degree angle of attach:

Fin force @ 5 degree angle of attack = [cosine (5) * (2.2)] + [sine (5) * (122)]

Fin force @ 5 degree angle of attack = [(0.996) * (2.2)] + [(0.087) * (122)]

Fin force @ 5 degree angle of attack = 2.19 + 10.6 = 12.8 lbs

So, if our rocket turns five degrees from the flight path just at motor burn out, the force on the fins trying to break them off will be about 13 lbs. This is not too bad. If the angle gets up to 10 degrees, then the force is about 23 lbs. In this case, it may be wise to use aluminum angle and nuts and bolts to hold the fins on.

Nosecones

Nosecones can be in almost any geometric shape. However, some of the most common shapes are ogive, tangent ogive, secant ogive, parabola and ellipse. The equations that define their contour are listed below:

Ogive:

$$Y = (D/2) * \{1-[(X+B)/A]^P\} * \{(A^P)/[(A^P)-(B^P)]\}$$

B greater than zero and less than L for a secant ogive

Tangent ogive:

$$Y = (D/2) * \{(1-([X/L]^P)\}$$

Parabola:

$$Y = (D/2) * [1-(X/L)]^P$$

Ellipse

$$Y = \{[D/2]^P * (1-[X/L]^P)\}^{(1/P)}$$

Where:

Y = Radius of nosecone at distance X
D = Diameter of nosecone at body tube
L = Length of nosecone outside of body tube
X = Distance along nose cone measured from body tube joint
P = Power (Equals 2 for a true ogive and 0.5 for a true parabola)
B = Distance that the ogive contour is translated into the body tube
A = L + B

Nosecones may be the most difficult part for the amateur to make unless you have a lathe. If you were going to make your own nosecone on a lathe, balsa wood or a soft pine would be the best material. I would recommend balsa since it is much lighter. Balsa wood can be purchased in blocks as large as four inches by four inches in lengths up to 48 inches. If you are going to make a nosecone with a diameter four inches or larger, you will have to glue blocks together. This will make a piece big enough to turn on the lathe. You can use standard techniques to glue the pieces together such as Elmer's Carpenter wood glue and clamps.

The only tricky part about turning balsa wood on a lathe is that it doesn't have much shear strength. The end of the lathe turning the wood will tear the wood unless you turn the wood at a slightly higher than normal speed. It is also important to use a light touch with the tools, as you do not want the balsa wood to grab and tear on the lathe spindle. You cannot use the same pressure as you would when turning pine as the tool will grab the balsa and stop it from turning.

Many amateur rocketeers buy commercial nosecones from a variety of high power rocketry suppliers. These companies have body tubes, nosecones, couplers and other supplies needed to make rockets, which are all compatible with themselves. The nosecones from these companies are made of molded plastic in a variety of shapes and sizes. Appendix G lists potential suppliers.

Mounting The Rocket Motor
Chapter 17

The rocket body has been sized for your flight. The next step is to make provision for mounting the motor inside the body tube. This can be done in one of two basic ways. The first method is to install motor centering rings and motor tubes so that the motor just slides into a tube, Figure 17-1. This method is most commonly used in high power rocket kits where the motor tubes are sized for standard chamber diameters. Kit manufacturers even put in mounting provision for clustering motors. The major disadvantage of this method is that if you want to install different motor diameters in the body tube, you have to rip out all previous motor mounts. This is a major inconvenience.

The second motor mounting method puts centering spacers onto the motor so that the body tube acts as a motor tube, Figure 17-2. With this method, you can use any motor chamber diameter as long as its diameter does not exceed the inside diameter of the body tube. Locate three spacers on each end of the motor with each spacer being 120 degrees from the previous one, Figure 17-3. You can wrap masking tape circumferentially around the spacers to adjust the diameter for a snug fit inside the body tube.

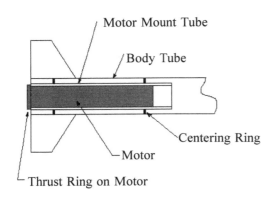

Figure 17-1: Motor Mount with Centering Rings and Motor Mount Tube

Besides centering the motor relative to the body tube, the motor mounts transfer the thrust of the motor into the body tube. One way to do this is to put a thrust ring on the aft end of the motor. If you are using a motor tube type system, then the ring will push against the aft bulkhead of the motor mount. The thrust load is then transferred to the bulkhead, which then transfers it to the body tube. It is important that the bulkhead be thick enough to take the thrust load. Also, the bulkhead must be securely fastened to the body tube.

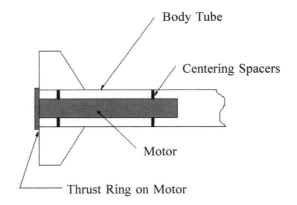

Figure 17-2: Centering Spacers Bonded to Motor

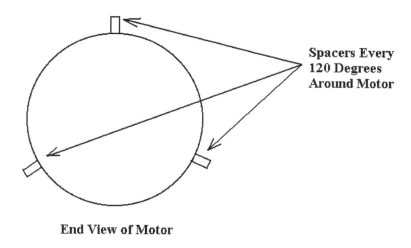

**Spacers Every
120 Degrees
Around Motor**

End View of Motor

Figure 17-3: End View of a Motor With Mounting Spacers

If your centering spacers are on the motor, you have a couple of options. First, you can make a thrust ring large enough in diameter so that it rests against the body tube outer diameter. With this method, the thrust of the motor is transferred directly to the body tube. If your motor is made of PVC pipe and fittings, you can cut a ring of PVC and glue it to the aft coupling to make a thrust ring, Figure 17-4.

Another way is to put a bolt through the body tube so that the motor's forward end is against the bolt. The thrust of the motor is transferred to the bolt and then into the body tube. The down side of this approach is that if you fly different length motors in the same rocket, the side of the body tube may start looking like Swiss cheese after awhile. One method I have used with good success on larger rockets is to wrap plumbers strap around the motor in the axial direction and duct tape it in place. The ends of the strap come out the bottom of the body tube and the two ends are then bolted to the body tube.

The other important thing about mounting the motor is to make provision for it not to fall out of the body tube. This can be done by friction fit of the motor in the tube or motor mount tube. You can also put a layer of tape around the motor thrust ring and body tube, if you are not using motor mount tubes. Another way is to use a retaining clip or a ring, which is attached to the body tube and goes over the aft end of the motor.

Figure 17-4: PVC Thrust Ring (Shown by Arrow) Bonded onto PVC Nozzle Fitting

Recovery Systems
Chapter 18

In the old days of amateur rocketry, people did not concern themselves with recovery systems. The rocket simply went up on a long arcing trajectory and crashed into the ground. Recovery in those days, was finding fragments or the bent up hull of your rocket. Things have changed since the "good ole days". For safety and sometimes to bring a payload section intact, amateur rockets usually have a parachute or streamer recovery. In this chapter, we are going to assume you want to recover your rocket intact.

The basic method of deploying a parachute or streamer is not much different than what is used in model rockets. At some point in the flight, an ejection charge goes off which blows the nosecone off the rocket and deploys a parachute or streamer. The difference in amateur rockets is that with the usually larger sizes and weights, you can use more sophisticated methods of setting off the ejection charge and deploying multiple parachutes.

<u>Delay Propellant Grains</u>

With small motors in small diameter rockets, you are pretty much stuck with using delay grains for timing the parachute deployment. They work fairly well and when they occasionally don`t, you aren`t out a whole lot of money. The rockets and motors in this size class are pretty cheap to make. The basic operation of the delay grain is that it ignites with the motor propellant and burns a slightly longer time. At that time, the flame front on the delay grain reaches a black powder ejection charge, which ignites and deploys the parachute or streamer.

How Long To Make The Delay Grain

One of the tricky parts of the delay grain approach is, "How long do I make it for a particular time?" First, you have to ask another question, "At what time after lift-off will the rocket reach peak altitude?" To answer this question, you can run FLIGHT for your motor and see at what time you reach maximum altitude. At that point, you want to deploy the parachute. Let`s suppose for your rocket, it is 15 seconds from lift-off and the motor burns for 5 seconds. So, you want the delay grain to burn for 10 seconds after motor burnout.

The determination of the required delay grain length is divided into two parts. The amount consumed during the motor firing and the amount consumed while the rocket is coasting up to maximum altitude. If we make the delay grain with the same propellant formulation used in the motor, it is fairly easy to calculate the delay grain length.

Delay Length = (Length Consumed During Firing) + (Length Consumed While Coasting)

First, the amount of delay grain consumed during the motor firing is simply the maximum web thickness inside the motor. If our motor is a straight core or segmented core motor with a web thickness of 3/8 inch, then 3/8 inch of delay grain will be consumed by motor burnout. If we have a C-slot or Moon burner, it would be the maximum web thickness. For our example, we are going to use a web thickness of 3/8 inch.

Delay Consumed During Firing = Maximum Propellant Grain Web Thickness

Note: Delay & Propellant are the same formulation

To calculate the grain length consumed while the rocket is coasting, you need to know the burn rate of the delay propellant at atmospheric pressure. To determine this you can take a piece of the propellant and cut it into a stick one inch long and about 3/8 inch diameter. Coat all sides of the propellant with high temperature RTV rubber except one of the small ends, Figure 18-1. After the RTV has fully cured, light the exposed end of the propellant and record the propellant burn time. Divide the propellant length (one inch) by the burn time and you have the burn rate for the delay grain when the rocket is coasting in flight. It will be slow. A typical ammonium nitrate propellant burn rate would be 0.017 inches per second.

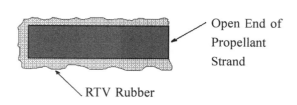

Open End of Propellant Strand

RTV Rubber

Figure 18-1: RTV Coating on Propellant Strand

The required delay grain length after motor burnout can be calculated knowing the burn rate and desired rocket coasting time. Our desired coasting time is 10 seconds and let's say the burn rate is 0.017 inches per second. Then:

Delay Length Consumed While Coasting = (Coast Time) * (Burn Rate)

Delay Length Consumed While Coasting = 10 * 0.017 = 0.17 inches

The total delay length can now be calculated using the previous formula:

Total Delay Length = (3/8) + (0.17) = 0.375 + 0.17 = 0.545 inches

From these calculations, the delay grain will fire the ejection charge 10 seconds after the main propellant grain is done firing or 15 seconds after motor ignition. Remember delay grains are approximate and will usually vary a second or two. A static firing of the motor will permit you to time the delay and confirm your calculations.

The actual methods of putting the delay grain in your motor are discussed in Chapter 11. Let's suppose, you've cast the delay grain and it's too long. That does not have to be problem. Taking a 1/4 inch diameter drill bit and making a hole in the exposed end of the delay grain can adjust it. The depth of the hole should be sufficiently deep so that the remaining undrilled length of delay grain is the desired delay grain length.

Drill Depth = (Total Delay Grain Length) - (Desired Delay Grain Length)

Using our previous example, suppose we actually cast a delay grain length of 1.5 inches and we really want a delay grain length of only 0.545 inches. Then:

Drill Depth = 1.5 - 0.545 = 0.955 inches

If you drill the hole to a depth of 0.955 inches, then your delay time should be about right. When you make the hole, drill it out slowly without letting the drill bit heat up. It is best to hand drill the hole holding the drill bit in your fingers. Take the drill bit in your hand and slowly rotate it with your fingers to make the hole. Drill out the hole a little bit and then remove the bit. Use your fingers to remove propellant in the grooves of the bit and throw the propellant filings away.

Electronic Activation of Ejection Charges

Electronic methods of activating the ejection charge fall into three basic categories, (1) electronic timers, (2) peak altitude sensing and (3) minimum velocity/g-force sensing. The electronic timers are essentially electronic delay grains, but are more reliable and accurate. The major drawback to timers is that you need to know at what time the rocket will reach peak altitude in order to set the timer. This requires an accurate knowledge of your motor's thrust-time curve, drag coefficient and accurate software to calculate the rocket's trajectory. That is not as bad as it sounds as you can usually determine these things so that your time will be accurate to within a couple of seconds. You will find if you play with the numbers, that an error of a few seconds will not result in a catastrophic deployment of the parachute.

Figure 18-2: Electronics Unit Mounted on Cardboard for Peak Altitude Parachute Deployment

The second method is based on measuring the altitude of the rocket on the way up. When the rocket reaches peak altitude and starts to descend, the ejection charge is set off. This method offers the advantage of not having to calculate a trajectory. These systems arm themselves when they experience a preset acceleration or climb a few hundred feet above ground level. Some of the more expensive models will also deploy a secondary chute at a lower altitude, usually around 750 ft above ground level. This enables you to use a drogue and main parachute system.

Figure 18-3: *Top* - Electronic Unit Going into Coupler; *Bottom* - Coupler Sealed by End Cap with Electronic Unit Inside

A key part of installing a pressure sensor recovery system is to install it in a chamber of the rocket, which is sealed on the aft and forward ends. The number of pressure holes and their diameters is based on manufacturers directions. The electronic boards should be mounted on another material so they are well supported for the forces of flight, Figure 18-2. The unit is mounted vertically inside a chamber of the rocket, which can be a sealed coupler, Figure 18-3.

The third electronic method measures acceleration forces on the rocket using an accelerometer. It converts acceleration into velocity and altitude. As with the second method, when peak altitude is reached it activates the ejection charge. Some of

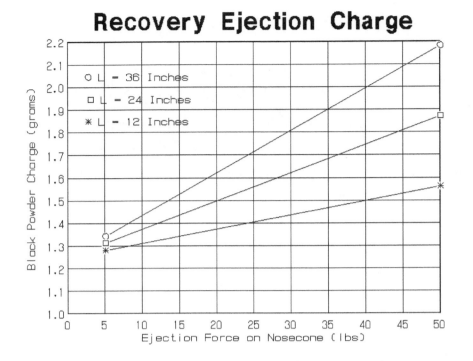

Recovery Ejection Charge

O L = 36 Inches
□ L = 24 Inches
* L = 12 Inches

Black Powder Charge (grams) — vertical axis: 1.0 to 2.2
Ejection Force on Nosecone (lbs) — horizontal axis: 0 to 50

Figure 18-4: Black Powder (4f) Ejection Charge for Parachute
Deployment

the models have a timer and/or pressure sensor for a secondary charge so you can have a drogue and main parachute system.

Manufacturers of the different types of electronic deployment systems offer units that measure altitude with time and peak altitude and store the data. Peak altitude data is usually read out to the user with a series of beeps from the electronic board while the altitude versus time data can be downloaded into a computer for examination.

Ejection Charge

The ejection charge is simply 4f black powder. The amount of black powder to use for a given rocket can be estimated, if we assume the body tube cavity will be instantly pressurized and that the gas does not lose any thermal energy to the body tube walls. Searching the literature, black powder has a flame temperature of 3307° R with a gas constant of 22.16 (ft-lbf)/(lbm - R). We can also assume the cavity to be pressurized is a cylinder and that the gas behaves as a "perfect gas". Using these relationships as a guide we developed an expression for the amount of black powder required to generate a given ejection force on the rocket's nosecone. We then ran experiments with different body tube sizes and nosecone weights to correlate the relationship with the experimental data. From those tests, we have refined our equation as follows:

Black Powder (grams) = [0.000517 * (Desired Ejection Force) * (Cavity Length)] + 1.25

The desired ejection force is in pounds and the cavity length is in inches. This equation has also been plotted for you and is shown in Figure 18-4. The important parameter for the ejection force is simply the length of the cavity to be pressurized by the ejection charge. It is important to note that the amount of charge shown in Figure 18-4 assumes that the body tube is sealed and that the nosecone fits snuggly into the body tube. If you have gas leakage then you will have to increase the amount of black powder.

The ejection force on the nosecone is also equal to the cross-sectional area of the nosecone base multiplied by the pressure in the body tube. We can use this relationship to calculate the body tube pressure for a given ejection force:

Body Tube Pressure (psi) = [4 * (Ejection Force)]/[3.14 * (Inside Body Tube Diameter)²]

The ejection force is in pounds and the inside body tube diameter is in inches.

To size the ejection charge, we need to know the desired ejection charge force. We can calculate the maximum required ejection force and use that as a guideline. If the rocket comes in ballistic or in a free fall condition, it will accelerate until the aerodynamic force on the rocket equals its weight. So the weight of the rocket at burnout is the maximum aerodynamic force to be expected for a typical rocket flight. This would not be the case if you were leaving the earth's atmosphere on an altitude shot, but that is another story. The ejection charge must also overcome the frictional force of the nosecone in the body tube. This force is usually only a pound or two.

Maximum Required Ejection Force = (Rocket Burnout Weight) + (Nosecone Friction Force) + (Something More)

The "Something More" is necessary to move the nosecone out of the body tube. If the ejection force just equals the aerodynamic and frictional forces, then the nosecone will not move. You need a little more force to eject the nosecone. Let's say our rocket weighs 8 lbs at burnout and the frictional force required to pull out the nosecone is 0.5 lbs, then the maximum required ejection charge must be something slightly more than 8.5 lbs. Perhaps, nine pounds would be right.

Of course, we have assumed the worse case. If the ejection charge goes off at the point when the rocket just reaches peak altitude, the aerodynamic forces are very low and 8.5 lbs would probably be overkill. The bottom line is that the amount of ejection force is up to you within these limits. With an electronic deployment system, you can be fairly sure that the charge will be activated at about peak altitude when aerodynamic forces are at a minimum. If you are using a delay grain, you may be wise to consider maximum ejection forces.

Suppose we have decided to play it safe and go with an ejection force of nine pounds for a three inch diameter rocket. The cavity length to be pressurized is 3 ft or 36 inches. Then, the required amount of black powder (4f) is:

Black Powder = [0.000517 * 9 * 36] + 1.25 = 0.17 + 1.25 = 1.42 grams

The resultant pressure in the body tube would be:

Body Tube Pressure = [4 * 9]/[3.14 * (3)²] = 36/[3.14 * 9] = 36/28.26 = 1.27 psi

There are a couple of important things to remember when using this amount of black powder. First, this is the amount of black powder required to blow the nosecone off the body tube when the body tube has a 1/8 inch vent hole and is sealed on the base end. Second, you must pack your parachute so that it fits loosely in the body tube. Don`t wad it up and cram it into the body tube. Third, the lines from the parachute to the nosecone should be wrapped around the parachute so that the nosecone will pull out the parachute when it is ejected out of the body tube.

Sizing the Parachute

The final thing to determine for your recovery system is the parachute size. In order to size the chute, you need to determine how fast you want the rocket to come down. A typical range is 17 to 22 ft/second. Let`s say your rocket can take 22 ft/second or 15 miles per hour. That`s a pretty good impact. To get a feel for it, drive by a wall at 15 miles per hour and throw your rocket out the window at the wall. Think it will survive? If not, you can use a lower number for your rocket. The burnout weight will be 8 lbs. The same relationship for calculating aerodynamic drag can be used for calculating the chute diameter. The parachute will accelerate with the rocket until the aerodynamic force on the chute equals the weight of the rocket. Then:

Chute Area = [64.4* (Rocket Weight)]/[(Air Density) * (Drag Coeff.) * (Descent Speed)²]

The rocket weight is in pounds; the descent speed is in ft/second and air density in lbm/ft³. We can use the formula in Chapter 1 for calculating the air density for our rocket descent. A range of drag coefficients for different parachutes is given in Table 18-1.

Let`s say our rocket is going to an altitude of 4,000 ft above ground level and that our launch site is 6,000 ft above sea level. If the parachute is deployed at peak altitude, then the

18-7

maximum altitude is 10,000 ft above sea level (4,000 + 6,000 = 10,000). The ground is 6,000 ft above sea level, so the average altitude we use for our calculations is halfway between 6,000 and 10,000, which is 8,000 ft above sea level. For our rocket, we are going to use a hemispherical chute and go for a descent rate of 22 ft/second. The air density is then:

Drag Coefficients for Parachutes

Table 18-1

Type of Parachute	Drag Coefficient Range
Flat Circular	0.75 - 0.80
Hemispherical	0.62 - 0.77
X-Form	0.60 - 0.85
Conical	0.75 - 0.90
Bi-Conical	0.75 - 0.92
Tri-Polyconical	0.80 - 0.96
Top Flight Round (9"-24")	1.09
Top Flight Round (30"-58")	1.34
Top Flight Round (70"-120")	1.40
Top Flight Cross (18"-80")	0.98

$$\text{Air Density} = 0.075 * \exp. (-7.4 \times 10^{-6} * [8000]^{1.15}) = 0.075 * \exp. (-7.4 \times 10^{-6} * 30800)$$

$$\text{Air Density} = 0.075 * \exp. (-0.22792) = 0.075 * 0.796 = 0.0597 \text{ lbm/ft}^3$$

Knowing the air density, we can calculate the required parachute area:

$$\text{Chute Area} = [64.4 * 8]/[0.0597 * 0.77 * (22)^2] = 515.2/[0.0597 * 0.77 * 484]$$

$$\text{Chute Area} = 515.2/22.25 = 23.16 \text{ ft}^2$$

We can convert chute area into a parachute diameter using the following equation:

$$\text{Parachute Diameter} = \text{Square Root } [(4 * \text{Chute Area}) / 3.14]$$

$$\text{Parachute Diameter} = \text{Square Root } [(4 * 23.16) / 3.14] = \text{Square Root } [92.64/3.14]$$

$$\text{Parachute Diameter} = \text{Square Root } [29.5] = 5.4 \text{ ft}$$

So, we would be looking for a hemispherical parachute about 5.4 ft or 64.8 inches in diameter. Unless you are making your own, you will have to buy from a commercial source that has stock diameters. You can check the stock chute diameter by calculating a descent rate and deciding if you can live with that descent rate. If not, go up the next chute size.

Recovery Zone

An important question to answer is, "How big of a recovery zone will I need?" The first thing to do is to run FLIGHT with a couple of launch angles to see what the ballistic dispersion of the rocket may be. This will be the case where the parachute does not come. You may want to look at angles up to five degrees. Look at the distance downrange when the rocket reaches peak altitude and the parachute deploys. Let's say that distance is 2000 feet. From that point, the parachute will deploy and the rocket will start drifting in the wind.

Suppose the rocket reached a peak altitude of 4000 feet and starts to descend on a parachute. A question that might pop up in our mind is, "How far will it drift in the wind?" Let's take a worse case of 20 mph winds, which is a wind speed of about 29 ft/second. Once the parachute is deployed and the rocket reaches equilibrium speed, the rocket will drift at the speed of the wind. We picked 22 ft/second as the maximum descent rate for our rocket based on impact damage or a desire not to have impact damage. If we know the time from deployment until the rocket lands, we can calculate the wind drift.

The time until the rocket lands can be calculated by dividing the altitude by the descent speed. For our case:

Descent Time = (Maximum Altitude)/(Descent Speed) = 4,000/22 = 182 seconds

The amount of drift is equal to the descent time multiplied by the wind speed:

Maximum Amount of Drift = (Descent Time) * (Wind Speed) = 182 * 29 = 5278 ft

That's just about a mile of parachute drift. We have to add the distance from the launch pad to parachute deployment to get a total downrange of 7278 feet.

Total distance downrange = (Distance of parachute deployment) + (Parachute drift)

Usually, the rocket will weathercock into the wind and cut that distance down some, but you cannot count on that. If that walk is a bit discouraging, you may want to consider a drogue parachute and then deploy the main parachute at a lower altitude. A good altitude to deploy the main would be about 750 ft above ground level. Let`s examine how a drogue and then main chute could reduce your hiking distance.

We could size a drogue parachute so that your descent rate was about 60 mph or 88 ft/second. From an altitude of 4000 ft to 750 ft, the descent distance would be the difference of these two numbers or 3250 ft. The descent time on the drogue would be:

Drogue Descent Time = (Drogue Drop Distance)/(Drogue Descent Speed)

Drogue Descent Time = 3,250/88 = 37 seconds

The descent time on the main would be the drop distance on the main, 750 ft, divided by the main descent speed, which was 22 ft/second.

Main Descent Time = (Main Drop Distance)/(Main Descent Speed)

Main Descent Time = 750/22 = 34 seconds

The total descent time for the rocket is equal to the drogue chute and main chute descent times or 37 seconds plus 34 seconds to equal 71 seconds. Now, the drift will be:

Maximum Drift (Drogue & Main) = 71 seconds * 29 ft/sec. = 2059 ft

Distance downrange = 2000 + 2059 = 4059 ft or about 0.77 miles.

With the drogue and main parachutes, we can cut the recover zone from about 1.5 miles to a little less than a mile. With weather cocking, the distance will probably be less than this. It is interesting to note that even if the rocket came screaming in towards the launch pad and deployed the main at 750 ft above the pad, the drift would still be about 1000 ft in a 20 mph wind.

Rocket Stability - Fin Design
Chapter 19

This is the final step in designing your rocket. Now, what kind of fins do you need and how big should you make them so that your rocket will be stable in flight. In order for your rocket to be stable in flight, the center of pressure must be aft of the center of gravity on your rocket. First, it`s important to understand what the center of gravity and center of pressure are before proceeding.

The center of gravity is the point inside your rocket where all the forces of gravity acting on your rocket are balanced out to zero. It doesn`t mean that the forces are zero, just that weight on one side of the center of gravity is balanced out by the weight on the other side. This is the precise point where the rocket will balance if suspended from this point. As you might suspect, that`s a pretty good way of finding the center of gravity of your rocket, simply find the point where it will balance.

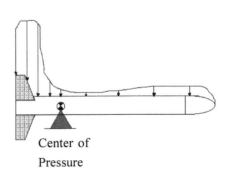

Center of
Pressure

Figure 19-1: Center of Pressure - Balance
of Aerodynamic Forces

The center of pressure is the point on your rocket where all the aerodynamic forces on the rocket balance out to zero. Again, it doesn`t mean that the aerodynamic forces are zero, just that there is a point on the rocket where wind force on one half of the rocket is balanced by the wind force on the other half. To visualize it in a simple way, imagine your rocket is like a teeter-totter with aerodynamics forces on both ends. If we move the pivot point of the teeter-totter to where it will just balance, that is the center of pressure, Figure 19-1.

The center of pressure must be aft of the rocket`s center of gravity for the rocket to be stable. Why? Remember from Chapter 1 that the rocket will pivot about its center of gravity. The aerodynamic forces in flight can be reduced to a single force that will act at the center of pressure. The airflow around the rocket is flowing from the forward end to the aft end, so when this is reduced to a single aerodynamic force, it is pushing from forward toward the aft end. To visualize this, imagine your rocket at a slight angle to the wind. If the center of pressure is forward of the center of gravity or pivot point, the air pushing from forward to aft will swing the rocket around so that the nose is pointing

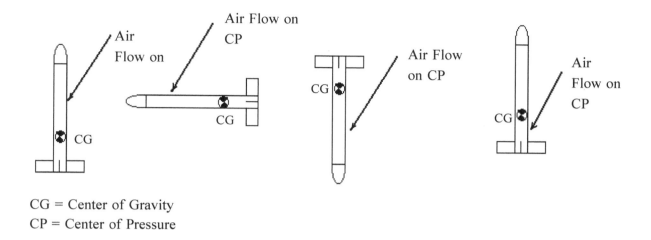

CG = Center of Gravity
CP = Center of Pressure

Figure 19-2: Influence of Center of Pressure Relative to Center of Gravity on Flight Stability

backwards, Figure 19-2.   This would obviously be an unstable condition since the rocket would try to fly with the nosecone as the caboose.   With the center of pressure aft of the center of gravity, the force of the air pushing aft keeps the nose pointed in the direction of flight. If that seems too complicated, look at it another way.   For the rocket to be stable in flight, the sum of the aerodynamic forces forward of the center of gravity must be less than the sum of the aerodynamic forces aft of the center of gravity.

Since we are not going to be putting an active guidance system in our rocket, we will need to rely on the fins to keep the rocket stable.   Fins are a simple way of moving the center of pressure aft of the center gravity.   When the rocket pivots, the flat surface of the fins move into the air flowing down around the rocket.   As more of the flat surface moves into the airflow, a larger and larger force is created which pushes against the body tube where the fins are attached.

Now, a tricky thing about the center of gravity and the center of pressure is that they are moving on the rocket during the flight.   As the solid propellant is burned, the aft end of the rocket gets lighter and the center of gravity moves forward.   While this is happening, the center of pressure is usually moving aft as the rocket goes faster and faster.   Why? Well, the correcting force from the fins increases with the air velocity squared.   That means if the air velocity is increased by two, the fin correcting force is increased by four.   If the air velocity is increased by three, the fin correcting force is increased by nine.   As the velocity of the rocket increases, the force of this air flowing down the sides of the rocket becomes dominant compared to wind forces. This leads us to static stability versus dynamic stability or stability on the launch rod versus stability in flight.

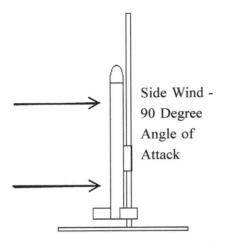

Figure 19-3: Rocket on Pad with Side Wind

Determining the Center of Pressure on Your Rocket

Determining the center of pressure for your rocket should be done for the conditions of sitting on the launch pad (90o angle of attack) and in flight (low angle of attack). Today, with personal computers, it is a fairly easy thing to do and as you will see, important, if you want your rocket to fly straight and true. We have included the Aerolab freeware on the software CD. This program will calculate the static and dynamic center of pressure for you. The program CP-1 is also included on the CD. It can be used for simple rocket shapes.

Static Stability

Static stability is essentially the stability of the rocket when the airflow comes at the rocket from the side. This is equivalent to an angle of attack of 90°, Figure 19-3. You can calculate the center of pressure for this situation using the software included with the book or use the "cardboard cut out" approach. The center of pressure can be closely approximated by determining the point where the projected area is equal on both sides, Figure 19-4. The cardboard cut out method determines this by cutting the silhouette of the rocket on a sheet of cardboard of constant thickness. Then you find the balance point of the sheet of cardboard with your rocket profile. The balance point is the center of pressure at a 90° angle of attack or when your rocket is sitting on the launch pad.

If the static center of pressure is aft of your rocket's center of gravity, then your rocket will be stable on the pad and during flight. You don't need to even look at flight stability if you don't want to. If the static center of pressure is forward of your center of gravity, don't worry yet. The only important thing is that it be aft of the center of gravity during flight or just as the rocket leaves the launch rod. Remember, as the rocket accelerates up the launch rod the center of pressure will be moving aft from its static position.

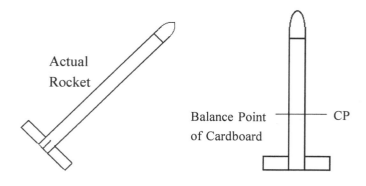

Figure 19-4: Static Stability Determined by the Cut Out Method

The dynamic stability of the rocket does not take full effect until the rocket reaches about 40 ft/second. Consequently, dynamic stability is more difficult to calculate. It requires determining the center of pressure through a summation of the aerodynamic forces on the rocket during flight at a given angle of attack and speed. Mr. Jim Barrowman in the 1960`s developed a systematic approach to determining the center of pressure at low angles of attack during flight. While it can be done by hand, the easiest method is to use the included software to calculate the center of pressure for your rocket. If this center of pressure is aft of your center of gravity, then your rocket will be stable in flight. If the center of pressure is forward of the center of gravity, then you will have to change your fin design or shift your center of gravity. The center of gravity can be shifted forward on the rocket by adding nose weight. Personally, I don`t see the point of adding weight to a rocket. I would change the fin size, unless you are doing a scale model of a rocket. In that case, you don`t have the option of changing the rocket`s shape; you will have to add weight to the nose.

Fin Design/Sizing

We've gone through and talked about determining the stability of your rocket. In order to do that, you have to have a fin size and number of fins. Most rockets are either three or four fin designs. The following simple formula for individual fin area will give you a starting point for your rocket:

For 3 Fins: Individual Fin Area = 0.17 * [(d + 0.5) * L]

For 4 Fins: Individual Fin Area = 0.13 * [(d + 0.5) * L]

d = Outside diameter of body tube (Inches)
L = Length of rocket without nosecone (Inches)

Now this is the area of one fin, which more or less can be translated into just about any shape you want as long as the base of the fin is at least 1.5 times the outside diameter of the body tube. Suppose we have a three-fin rocket with a body tube that has an outside diameter of 3.25 inches. We are going to make it 48 inches long. Using the three-fin formula, we can calculate the area for one fin. Of course, each fin will be equal to this same area.

$$\text{Individual Fin Area} = 0.17 * [(d + 0.5) * L] = 0.17 * [(3.25 + 0.5) * 48]$$

$$\text{Individual Fin Area} = 0.17 * [3.73 * 48] = 0.17 * 180 = 30.6 \text{ in}^2$$

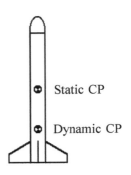

Figure 19-5: Position of Static and Dynamic Center of Pressure

So each fin should be 30.6 square inches. We can make it a rectangle, delta, clipped delta, triangle or whatever. The other important thing is that the base must be at least 1.5 times the body tube outside diameter or 4.875 inches (1.5 * 3.25 = 4.875). Suppose we make the fin a simple rectangle with a base of 5 inches, then the fin tip and fin root would be 6.12 inches (30.6 / 5 = 6.12). You can play with dimensions for a given body tube length and diameter for various fin shapes. When you have one that looks good, then run that shape for a flight and static center of pressure calculation using the included software. Of course, you could just play with fin shapes using the center of pressure software first. The choice is really up to you.

Maximum Permissible Angle of Attack

If your rocket is stable both statically and dynamically, then your maximum permissible angle of attack is 90 degrees. Your rocket can take virtually anything. As you might suspect, a rocket in this condition usually has large fins. Most people do not want to put big "honking" fins on their rockets for reasons of weight or just appearance. Over sized fins also make the rocket very sensitive to wind so it will turn into the wind almost instantly.

The best way to size your fins is based on dynamic stability, not static stability. This often means that your rocket is statically unstable. When your rocket is dynamically stable, but statically unstable, there is some angle of attack where the rocket will go from stable to unstable. We can make an estimate of this critical angle of attack.

Suppose our rocket has a center of gravity located 50 inches from the nose. We've calculated a static center of pressure that's 45 inches from the nose and a dynamic center of pressure that's 59 inches from the nose, Figure 19-5. We can relate the center of pressure based on angle of attack with the following expression:

Center of Pressure = Static Position + [Cosine (Angle of Attack) * ({Dynamic Position} - {Static Position)}]

Center of Pressure = 45 + [Cosine (Angle of Attack) * (59 - 45)]

Center of Pressure = 45 + [14 * Cosine (Angle of Attack)]

Suppose we have an angle of attack of 15 degrees, we can use this formula to determine the center of pressure for that condition on our rocket:

Center of Pressure = 45 + [14 * Cosine (15°)] = 45 + [14 * 0.97] = 45 + 13.58

Center of Pressure = 58.58 inches

The center of pressure would be 58.58 inches from the nose, which is aft of the center of gravity, so the rocket would be stable at an angle of attack up to 15 degrees. This angle of attack can be translated into a wind speed and rocket velocity. The tangent of the angle of attack is equal to the wind speed divided by the rocket's speed:

Tangent (Angle of Attack) = (Wind Speed) / (Rocket Speed)

Angle of Attack = Tangent^{-1} [(Wind Speed) / (Rocket Speed)]

Suppose the wind speed at launch is 15 miles per hour or 22 ft/second. If the launch rod is 7 ft long and the acceleration of the rocket is four g's, we can calculate the rocket's velocity leaving the rod.

Rocket Velocity = Square Root [2 * (arod) * (Rod Length)]

Rocket Velocity = Square Root [2 * (4 * 32.2) * 7] = Square Root [1803.2] = 42.5 ft/second

We can then calculate the angle of attack of the rocket off the launch rod:

Angle of Attack = Tangent^{-1} [(22) / (42.5)] = Tangent^{-1} [0.5176] = 27.37°

If this angle of attack were higher than the maximum allowed, the rocket would be unstable as it leaves the rod. Your option at this point would be to redesign the fins or come off the rod faster to decrease the angle of attack.

A Simple Launch Pad
Chapter 20

Your rocket is all done and so is the motor. Now you are ready to launch your rocket. One of the first things you will need is a launch pad to hold your rocket in a vertical position. You will also need a launch rod or rail to guide your rocket until sufficient aerodynamic forces build up on the fins to keep your rocket stable. In this chapter, we will give you instructions for a couple of simple launch pads you can make.

Just like smaller model rockets, you can use a launch rod to keep the rocket vertical on the initial part of ascent. You also use a launch lug or tube bonded to the side of the rocket for the rod to slide into, Figure 20-1. For very small rockets you can get away with one launch lug at the center of gravity of the rocket. However, for most high power rockets, I would recommend two launch lugs. One should be forward of the center of gravity and the other should be aft. Locate them so that when the launch rod goes through the lugs it is between the fins and not interfering with any bolts or other protuberances on the rocket.

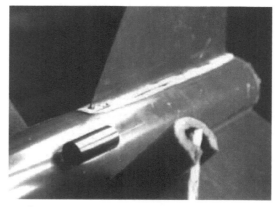

Figure 20-1: Launch Lug on Rocket

Typically, launch rods range from six to eight feet in length, but you can make yours longer if you want. This is particularly true if the rocket has a slow acceleration. Remember, you want your rocket traveling at about 40 ft/second when it leaves the rod. The next question is, "How big in diameter should the launch rod be?" This is really a function of the rocket's weight and motor impulse. I would not use anything smaller than a 3/8 inch rod for even a G class motor. For J class motors and rockets weighing up to 15 pounds, I would go with a ½ inch rod. For rockets weighing over 15 lbs, I would use a one inch diameter rod. I have launched rockets up to almost 40 lbs on a one inch rod with M class motors. A good measure of whether a rod is strong enough is to look at the flexibility of the rocket once it is on the rod. If the rod is bending or has a lot of flex to it, then you should move up to a larger diameter. Launch rods over one inch in diameter can be used for larger rockets, but at this point you may want to examine the use of launch rails. They are more rigid and can better support the larger rockets.

Launch rods are usually standard carbon steel, but you can use stainless steel, if you can afford it. The cheapest place to get rods is where they sell surplus steel. If you need a long rod, but cannot get it into your car or truck bed, you can take it to a machine shop and have them cut it into two sections. They can thread one end of the rod and drill and tap one end of the other rod. It should be set up so that one rod will screw into the other. Machine shops are expensive and expect to pay around $100 for this. You can also take a length of PVC pipe and make a carrier for your rods so that you or someone else doesn`t get poked in the face with the rod. Put end caps on each end, but don`t glue them onto the pipe. This way you can remove the rods for the PVC pipe when you are at the launch site.

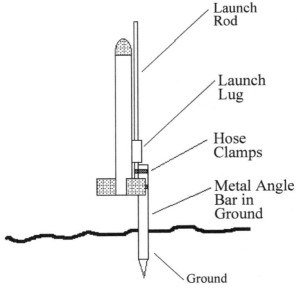

Figure 20-2: Simple Launch Pad with Launch Rod Attached to Metal Angle Bar Driven into the Ground

The simplest launch pad is shown in Figure 20-2. Here a piece of steel angle bar is driven into the ground in a vertical position. The launch rod sits in the V-notch of the angle bar and is held in place with two hose clamps. To make it easier to drive the angle bar into the ground, cut a point on one end with a hacksaw. A sledgehammer works best for driving it into the ground. You have to watch the angle of the bar as you drive it into the ground so it stays vertical. The rocket exhaust will hit the ground so make sure it is clear of dry grass or brush so you do not start a fire. While this pad is easy to set up, it can be a bear to pull the bar out of the ground when you are done for the day.

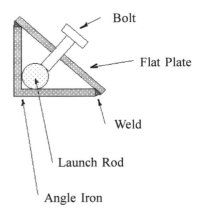

Figure 20-3: Top View of Flat Plate Attached to Angle Iron to Make Launch Rod Holder

A better stand uses a piece of angle iron that is attached to a flat plate with brackets and bolts or by welding. Weld two pieces of flat steel across the angle iron as shown in Figure 20-3. Drill and tap a hole in each flat piece for a 1/4-20 bolt. The launch rod goes into the angle iron and is held in place by the two bolts. The size of the angle iron depends on how large of a diameter launch rod you want to hold. The important thing is to make the base wide enough so that the rocket is stable and will not tip over before launch. To the bottom of the flat plate attach four pieces of angle iron sticking out in radial directions, Figure 20-4. The angle iron will be attached to the plate by bolts. Make each

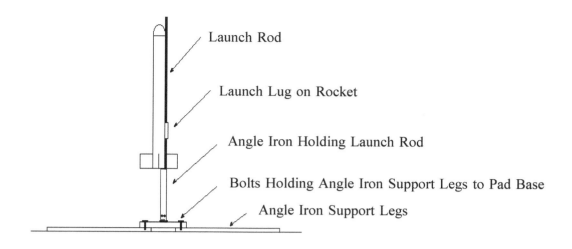

Launch Rod

Launch Lug on Rocket

Angle Iron Holding Launch Rod

Bolts Holding Angle Iron Support Legs to Pad Base

Angle Iron Support Legs

Figure 20-4: Launch Pad with Base and Angle Iron Support Legs

angle iron about 4 ft long. The rocket will sit on the vertical angle iron providing a nice standoff. The flat plate on the bottom also serves as a blast deflector. A variation of this is to weld three tubes onto the bottom of the flat plate, Figure 20-5. Into each of these tubes you can insert another tube, which will serve as a leg to make a tripod. The tubes can be held in place with bolts.

Of course, you can come up with your own design. The main thing is to have a stable platform so the rocket cannot tip over before launch. As your rockets get larger with more area facing into the wind, this will become a more significant problem.

Figure 20-5: Launch Pad with Tubular Legs

Electrical Ignition Systems
Chapter 21

In the old days of rocketry, a simple cannon fuse was all you needed to light your motor. To be safe, you should use an electrical ignition system to ignite your motors. The key part of the system is having a good battery with plenty of amperage so that your igniter will work properly. There is nothing more frustrating than having a good electrical system fail in making your igniters work due to a weak battery. A 12 volt car battery works very well.

The schematic for a simple system is shown in Figure 21-1. You can more or less select whatever switches you wish, but they must be rated for the amperage you can expect to flow through the firing circuit. Let's say your igniter has a resistance of 1.5 ohms and your line resistance in the firing circuit is 0.5 ohms. The total resistance in the firing circuit with the igniter attached will be sum of the two resistances or 2.0 ohms. Assuming you will be using a 12 volt DC battery, we can figure out the total amperage in the circuit using Ohm's law:

Line Current = Voltage/Resistance = (12 volts) / (2 ohms) = 6 amps.

Therefore, your switches should be rated for at least six amps. Actually, you do not want to use your switches at maximum capacity so make sure their rating is more than six amps. You can find automotive toggle and momentary toggle switches that are rated for 16 to 20 amps at 12 Volts DC in Radio Shack and automotive stores. You can also use AC switches rated for high amperage. However, you have to be careful as AC and DC switches are designed differently due to more internal arcing in DC applications than AC applications.

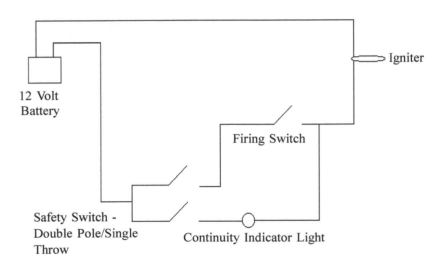

Figure 21-1: Schematic of Electrical Firing Ciruit

For the safety or continuity check switch, you can use a toggle switch. For the firing switch, use a momentary switch. You must hold this spring-loaded switch in the on position.

When you let go, it springs to the off position. The circuit shows a fuse or 12 VDC circuit breaker. This is very important as a car battery has enough amperage to melt down your firing control panel if you get a dead short. The amperage rating on the breaker or fuse should be between 15 and 20 amps. The

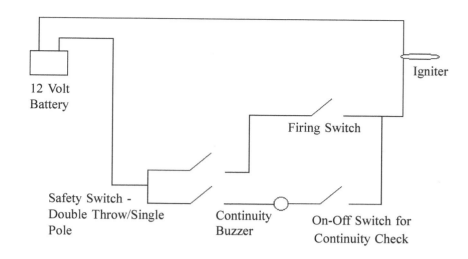

Figure 21-2: Firing Schematic with Continuity Buzzer

fuses should also be the "fast acting" kind. A circuit breaker is nicer than a fuse since it can be reset. If you use fuses, make sure you have a good supply at the launch site.

The circuit diagram shows an indicator light for showing the firing circuit is armed and that the system has continuity. The light can only go on if the firing circuit is all hooked up. The indicator light should draw only low amperage in the circuit. If the amperage is high, it could fire the igniter. While this is not likely for the nichrome wire igniters, it is possible for igniters using electric matches or flashbulbs to start an ignition sequence. Limit the continuity indicator to the lowest possible milliamp (mA) rating.

A problem with indicator lights is that they are often hard to see in the daylight. An alternative to the light is to use a piezo buzzer. This will provide an audible sound when the circuit is armed. If you don`t want to hear the buzzer going the whole time the circuit is armed, you can use the schematic in Figure 21-2. In this circuit, you will only hear the buzzer when the momentary continuity switch is flipped to the on position.

You can find project boxes at Radio Shack or other stores to put the entire firing circuit into and make a nice attractive control box. For the wiring to and from the control box, it is suggested that you use standard 120 VAC plugs and extension cords. For the line going from the control box to the launch pad, make a short lead out of the control box with a 120 VAC plug on the end. You can use extension cords in 100 foot lengths to run from the control box to the launch pad. For the launch pad end, make a cord with a 120 VAC plug on one end and a pair of alligator clips on the other. The extension cords can be a small as 16 gauge. The nice thing about this approach is that you can use your extension cords you have at home for your launch needs. If you need another 50 or 100 ft of length, just use another extension cord.

A second system locates the battery at the launch pad. This will prevent loss of power to the igniter due to long line from the battery to the igniter with the previous system. A schematic of this rely system is shown in Figure 21-3. The relay, fuse or circuit breaker, piezo buzzer

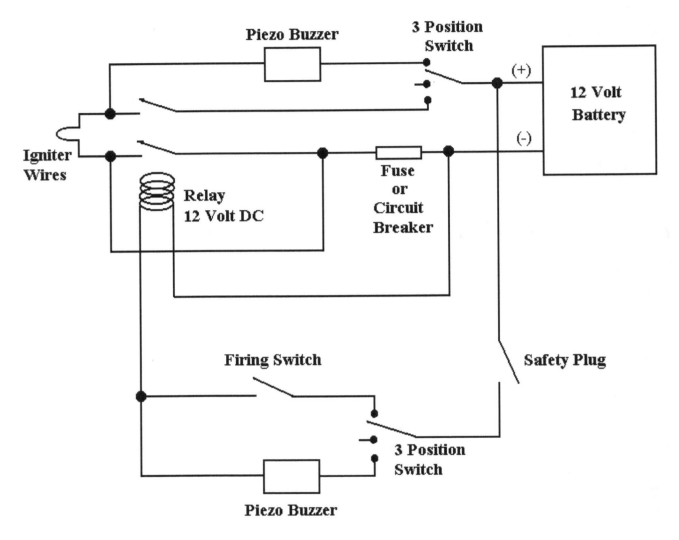

Figure 21-3: Firing Schematic With Relay

and test switch should be mounted inside a metal box that is tough enough to sit on the ground. The test switch is a three toggle switch that you can buy at Radio Shack. The relay should be an automotive type relay that is good for more amperage than the igniter could draw. It is important to put in the fuse or circuit breaker to protect the relay. If you do not, the relay can

21-3

be fuse closed during a short. If it fuses closed, power will always be going to the igniter clips. This will give you an unexpected thrill when you connect your next rocket up to the ignition system.

These are some basic electrical systems. You can make them more complicated or sophisticated if you wish. The important thing is that it be designed to reduce the chance of accidentally firing the igniter while being reliable in firing the igniter when the countdown reaches "Ignition!"

Making Your Own Igniters
Chapter 22

Igniting a composite propellant grain is source of frustration for many people. One good method of igniting these motors to use electric igniters dipped in a pyrogen. These can be homemade or purchased commercially. However, you can make another type of igniter out of composite propellant. It is rare for an igniter made from composite propellant to fail in igniting a composite propellant motor. You can make the igniters out of ammonium perchlorate or ammonium nitrate composite propellant. The important thing when igniting all composite propellant motors is to place the igniter in the most forward end of the motor bore. This will ensure your motor comes up to full power. If you ignite the propellant by the nozzle, your motor will not come up to full power.

If you are using ammonium nitrate or ammonium perchlorate propellant in your motors, take some of the excess from your casting and use that to make igniters. Ammonium perchlorate propellant will be easier to igniter and be a little more vigorous as an ignition material. For those of you making AN propellant, but want to use AP propellant in the igniter,

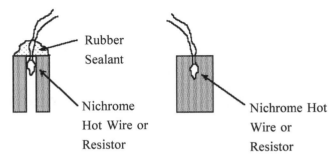

Figure 22-1: Two Basic Types of Igniters Using Composite Propellant

I would suggest an AP formulation of 77% AP, 8% aluminum powder (-325 mesh) and 15% R45HT binder.

Composite Propellant Igniters

Composite propellant igniters are electric igniters embedded in composite propellant. There are two basic types as shown in Figure 22-1. The first type is made by cutting cured propellant into small pieces with a sharp knife. Then, make a small hole all the way through the propellant that is the same diameter as a small resistor (10 ohm, ¼ or ½ watt) or 30 gauge nichrome wire coiled on a wire lead. Make the hole by hand using a drill bit of the required diameter and twisting it in your fingers. After the hole is made, insert the igniter wire into the hole.

The second type of composite propellant igniter is the best. The electrical igniter is embedded into the propellant before it cures. To make this type of igniter, get some plastic or paper straws. Cut the straws into 1.5 inch long pieces. Fill the straws with propellant by pushing the propellant into the straws with your fingers. You should wear plastic gloves while doing

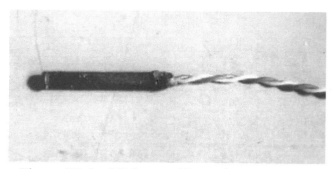

Figure 22-2: Nichrome Hot Wire Inside AN Composite Propellant

this. After filling the straws with propellant, insert the nichrome wire or resistor into the one of the straw. After the propellant has cured, cut the plastic or paper straw off the propellant. You can do this by making a long cut with a razor knife down the length of the straw and then peeling it off. Try to cut only the straw and not the propellant. The finished igniter will look like the one shown in Figure 22-2.

Making Electrical Igniters for Composite Propellant Igniters

Almost all igniters begin the ignition process with a hot wire to ignite a chemical, which in turn ignites something else. A reliable electrical hot wire source is to make your own using 30-gauge nichrome wire. First, cut 22-24 gauge twisted pair wire into two foot lengths. This will be your igniter lead. Then, cut one end of the wire about one inch shorter than the other, Figure 22-3. Cut a piece of 30-gauge nichrome wire about three inches long. Make a good mechanical connection to the inner exposed end of the igniter leads. Use a liquid flux on the connection and then solder it. Wrap the nichrome wire around the outer igniter lead wire to form a coil. Make sure the coils do not touch or the igniter will short out. Make enough windings so that the resistance across the igniter is about 1.5 ohms. You can measure the resistance with an ohmmeter or multimeter. When you have the right length, make a good mechanical connection of the free end of the nichrome wire to the outer igniter lead. Coat the connection with flux, solder it and cut off the free end of the nichrome wire.

Another method is to use a resistor type as a "hot wire"

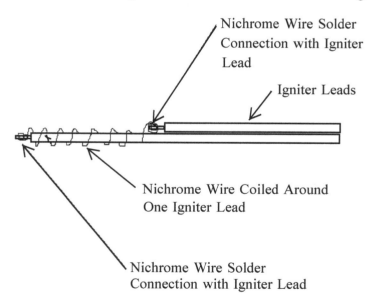

Nichrome Wire Solder Connection with Igniter Lead

Igniter Leads

Nichrome Wire Coiled Around One Igniter Lead

Nichrome Wire Solder Connection with Igniter Lead

Figure 22-3: Nichrome Hot Wire Schematic

source. It is simple to make and cheap. You can buy the 10-ohm, ¼ watt or ½ watt resistors from Radio Shack. When the electrical power from a car battery is supplied to the resistors, they pop and burst into flames. This ignites the composite propellant chunk which then igniters the propellant in the motor. These types of igniters are made the same way as the nichrome hot wire sources except a resistor is used instead of

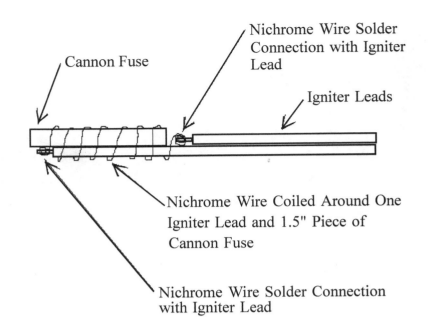

Figure 22-4: Cannon Fuse Igniter

nichrome wire. For this type of igniter, you will have to hold the ignition button down for several seconds before you hear the resistor pop and burst into flames. The ½ watt resistor takes the longest at about six seconds.

You will find that with AP composite propellant that heat from the nichrome wire does not have to be applied very long before it ignites. Ammonium nitrate propellants take a little longer application of heat before they ignite. You may experience the situation where your hot wire burns out before it ignites the AN propellant. If this is the case, make the resistance on the hot wire just a little higher so that it ignites the propellant before it burns out. You may have to do a little experimentation to find the right resistance value.

Cannon Fuse Igniters

This is another simple electrical igniter using nichrome wire and cannon fuse. You can buy cannon fuse at some sporting goods stores and from almost all pyrotechnic supply houses. It makes a small diameter igniter that will fit through a ¼ inch diameter throat. It is very reliable and easy to make. It is essentially the same as the nichrome hot wire source. In this case, the nichrome wire is wrapped around the igniter lead wire and a 1.5 inch long piece of cannon fuse, Figure 22-4. This igniter works very well with the 1 inch PVC pipe motor in Appendix A. For larger diameter bore motors, you can use two 1.5 inch long pieces of cannon fuse.

Bag Igniters

For large bore motors, you may want to use a bag igniter. It consists of a bag holding propellant shavings. The bag can made of cheese cloth or paper and should be tied closed with small diameter string or thread. Inside the bag is a composite propellant igniter, Figure 22-5. The igniter lights the propellant in the bag producing a very large heat source, which ignites the propellant grain.

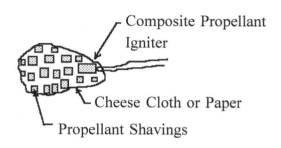

The propellant shavings are those produced when you drill out propellant cartridges. You do not need many shavings to produce a lot of flame and heat. For example, about four cups of propellant shavings was enough to ignite an eight inch bore motor that was about nine feet long. Take some propellant shavings and ignite them in the open air and you will see what I mean. It doesn`t take much. The important thing is not to get carried away and use too many propellant shavings in the bag. If you do, it is possible that you will over pressurize the chamber on ignition and blow up the motor.

Figure 22-5: Bag Igniter

Finding a Launch Site
Chapter 23

Now, that you've made all this great stuff to fly and got all the equipment needed to launch it, "where are you going to fly it?" Well, if you own a lot of land or have a close relative who does, you're all set.   If you are like most of us, you will have to find a launch site.   If your rocket and motor are small enough so that you don't need an FAA waiver (Chapter 27), you can use any field that you can get permission to use.   As far as field dimensions, that depends on how high you are going, how fast you will be descending on the parachute at a given wind speed.   Table 23-1 gives you an idea of recovery zones for different heights and wind speeds at a 15 ft/second descent.

Recover Zone Diameter Based on Height and Wind Speed
At 15 ft/second Descent

Table 23-1

Height	Descent Time (Sec.)	10 MPH	20 MPH
1000	67	0.37 miles	0.74 miles
3000	200	1.11 miles	2.22 miles
5000	333	1.85 miles	3.70 miles
7,500	500	2.78 miles	5.56 miles

As you can see, if you are planning to go high without a drogue/main parachute system, you are going to be looking for some big acreage.   In addition, this assumes you are going to be launching from the center of the diameter with the wind direction possibly coming from all directions.   In reality, there is usually a prevailing wind direction, which would permit you to shift the launch site to one side reducing the amount of land required for a launch site. Weathercocking will also work in your favor since the rocket will go into the wind and then drift back towards you.   Considering this, you may be able to knock those diameters in half and still be able to launch and recover within the site.   Still, you will be looking for a substantial piece of land if you plan to go 5000 ft above the ground.

Your land options come down to federal, state, county, city and private land.   Go to a sporting goods store that sells maps for hunting.   They will carry maps showing land owned by BLM (Federal Bureau of Land Management), the state and private owners.   The second map you will need is an aviation "Sectional Map".   You can get these at the nearest airport from the fixed-base operator. The fixed-based operator is usually the same company that gives flying lessons, rents planes, etc. This map will be handy for filing a waiver and for picking a launch site that has a minimum amount of air traffic over it. This is described in more detail in Chapter 27, but look at the map and you will see lines with a "V" and a number. These are called "Victor" airways and are commonly used by private planes that will be flying at low altitudes. These planes will be your number one headache so if you can pick a launch site not directly under one of these airways, you will have an easier time with your waiver. You will also see that these lines converge at different points, almost like an intersection. That`s about what they are, intersections for private planes in the sky. Guess how thrilled the FAA will be about your waiver application if your launch site is located in the middle of one of these intersections. Avoid them at all costs.

As you can imagine, you will need some room to spread your maps out and look at where the low flying planes will be versus public and private land. Against, this you must look at terrain. You don`t want to launch off the side of a mountain or in hilly country. When you are at the sporting goods store, get yourself a geological survey map that shows terrain. That is just what you wanted, more maps. Ok, you are out about $30 in maps and have them spread out on the floor.

First, you have to make a choice as to whether you want to go with government or private land. A good first choice would be BLM land if you have some in your area. For just yourself or a small group, you can go onto BLM land without needing a permit, as it is "casual use". It would still be a good idea to check with the local office and tell them what you plan to do. Usually, their main concern will be fire danger or possible damage to the land from your activities.

If you don`t have any BLM land that is suitable for a site, try the state. Each state is different and many states have virtually no land available. Check with your state land management office to see what their policy is on land use. If this doesn`t pan out, you are down to county and city land. These will usually be parcels of land too small for a launch site, but it is worth a shot. In addition, you will likely run up against more restrictions and a general "freak out" about liability exposure from the local government attorneys. That brings us to the last choice, private land.

Private land owners are going to be farmers, ranchers or land barons. As a group, these people have money and assets, which they are absolutely paranoid about losing. They will be very conscious of liability exposure and getting their rear end sued off by you, your relatives or somebody else you might bonk in the head with your rockets. If you approach a private landowner, stress safety and that you are by yourself or have an extremely small group. Also, that you will not damage the land and will clean up any mess you make afterwards. You have to raise their comfort level to the point where they will let you on the land. Bring rocket magazines and/or a video you can leave with them to look at so they can get a feel for what you want to do. But, don't leave them a crash and burn rocket video with heavy metal music playing in the background. If you can get them interested in the sport, that will greatly help your cause.

Ok, you have some sites in mind from looking at the maps. Next, you have to drive out and look it over. What looks good on the map may really be a doggy location on closer inspection. If it looks good, go to the appropriate agency or landowner and see if you can use it. If not, try a second site. You can expect this process to take a considerable amount of time, perhaps, a few months. The main thing about finding a launch site is you have to keep plugging away at it until you find something you can use. Don't be afraid to travel. It is not unusual for a launch site to be a few hours away by car.

The Big Day ...... Launch!!
Chapter 24

This is what it's all about, launching your rocket and seeing if all your assumptions, calculations and handiwork is correct and up to the job. The first thing you have to do when you get to your launch site is to set up your rocket preparation table. Although you could do it in the back of a truck or car, it is a lot easier if you set up a portable table to work on. You can also use this table for holding your electrical launch controller.

<u>Setting up the Launch Pad and Electrical System</u>

I would recommend that you set up your launch pad and associated electrical system before preparing your rocket for launch. You want to place the launch pad a safe distance from you so that if something goes wrong, you will not be in danger. A suggested list of distances versus motor impulse ranges is given in Table 24-1. This is just a suggested distance. If your motor or rocket is potentially risky or unreliable, you should probably extend these distances.

Distances from Launch Pad to Launch Controller
Table 24-1

Motor Impulse (lb-second)	Motor Type	Distance (feet)
36 - 72	H	50
73 - 144	I	100
145 - 288	J	100
289 - 576	K	200
577 - 1152	L	300
1153 - 2304	M	500
2305 - 4607	N	1000
4608 - 9215	O	1500

Once you have the launch system set up, I would recommend running a test with an igniter to make sure everything is working. You could also do it with a multimeter set to measure voltage.

Also, clear any brush from around the launch pad so that the exhaust plume from the rocket motor will not start any fires. As a general rule of thumb, clear a 10 ft radius around the launch pad of any dry brush or other material that may burn. If you are going to be launching large motors with a large exhaust flame, you may want to increase this radius.   Make sure you bring a couple of fire extinguishers and some water for putting out fires.

Preparing the Rocket for Launch

Once you have the launch pad and electrical system set up, it`s time to prepare your rocket for launch.   It will be easier to prepare your rocket if you make a little stand to hold your rocket horizontally.   You can make a simple one using PVC pipe, Figure 24-1.   For a complicated

Figure 24-1:   Rocket on PVC Pipe Rack

rocket, you may want to make a checklist of things that have to be done before the rocket can be launched.   You will be plenty nervous and it is easy to forget something if you have to do a lot of things.

If you are using an electronic deployment system, you will have to first load the ejection charge into a small tube with a flashbulb or electric match located in the bottom. These can be bought commercially or you can make your own.   You can also make a small bag for holding the powder and flashbulb or electric match.   Make sure the powder is retained at the bottom of the tube or bag where the flashbulb or electric match is located.   Place the charge in the recovery section of the body tube.   Follow manufacturers directions for the power up sequence relative to hooking up the ejection charge to the electronics.   Generally, the electronics are powered up first and allowed a minute to settle in before the charge is connected.

Load into the body tube cellulose material to help quench the flame from the ejection charge. This will help reduce damage to the parachute from the black powder charge when it goes off. Put in enough cellulose material to fill up about three to four body diameters worth of distance in the tube.   Don`t pack the cellulose into the tube as if you are ramming powder into a cannon barrel.   It should be relatively loose. Pack the parachute and load it into the body tube.   It is important that your parachute fit loosely inside the body tube and that it is pulls out when the nosecone is pulled out of the tube.   Don`t cram the parachute into the body tube.

Load the motor into the body tube and make sure it is retained in the tube.   Check your igniter for continuity with an ohmmeter.   If it shows infinite resistance, zero resistance or too high of a resistance, select another igniter.   Insert the igniter into the motor.   The igniter must be placed all the way to the forward end of the motor or the motor will not get up to full power. Tape the wire leads from the igniter so that they go off to the side of the rocket.

A helpful hint in making the preparation of your rocket easier is to do as much as you can at home. This would include installing the motor, making your ejections charges and if possible, packing your parachutes. It is amazing how even the simplest things can become difficult under field conditions where the wind is blowing.

<u>Launch</u>

Figure 24-2: Hooking Up Igniter Wires

Take your rocket out to the launch pad and insert it onto the launch rod. Attach your ignition wires to the igniter when you are sure the ignition system safe-arm is in the safe position, Figure 24-2. If you have a safe-arm switch or plug on the ejection charge of your rocket, pull it after hooking up the igniter. At this point, you are ready to walk back to your launch controller.

Check the sky for aircraft and the launch area for people or vehicles. If aircraft are in the area, wait before launching. If people or vehicles are in the recovery area that are not part of the launch, wait until they are clear. When the sky and range are clear, you can launch.

It is best to do a five second countdown before launching the rocket. Make sure everyone is aware you are launching. This way they will be ready for whatever happens. This is the moment of truth. Hopefully, the igniter will work and your rocket will roar into the sky. As is often the case, the igniter may not go off or it will go off, but not ignite the motor. In this case, wait at least a minute before going out to the pad. Make sure the launch system is returned to the "safe" position before proceeding. If the igniter fired, but did not ignite the motor, replace the igniter

Figure 24-3: Amateur Rocket Going Up

and try again. If the igniter did not fire, check your electrical lines for a short. The problem may also be a weak battery.

Once you have installed a new igniter or fixed your electrical system, try again. Make sure you check the sky and range again before launching. This time your rocket should come to life and roar off into the sky.

If at First You Don`t Succeed ......
Chapter 25

The big launch day has come; you press the firing button, hold your breath and wait to see what happens. Usually, you`ll see your rocket rise on a tail of flame and roar into the sky. Sometimes, you get something else. Don`t worry about it. Nobody has 100% success unless they keep doing the same thing over and over again. If your first rocket works perfectly, congratulate yourself. If it doesn`t, don`t give up. Fix the problem and try again. If you`ve static fired the motor successfully, failures are most likely going to be either rocket instability or a failure of the recovery system.

Figure 25-1: Recovered Wreckage from Rocket with Failed Recovery System

If your rocket takes off from the rod and starts pitching over until it is almost flying horizontally, then your rocket went into the "cruise missile" mode. The cause of this is that the rocket is underpowered; it needs more thrust off the rod. This can happen because the motor is just too weak or the throat could have suddenly opened, which will cause the thrust to drop off. Try a stronger motor or non-eroding throat in the next flight.

If it takes off like a bat out of hell and some time before motor burn out, the fins come off or the rocket seems to disintegrate, the aerodynamic forces were too great for the structure. If one of the fins comes off in flight, the rocket will suddenly pitch over and it will come apart due to flying sideways. If the flight looked normal up to the point of failure, strengthen the fin joint. If the rocket was flying in a zigzag fashion right before it came apart, it was probably due to the fins flexing in flight. Rebuild the rocket using a fin material that is not as flexible.

If the rocket comes off the rod and turns away from the wind and then flies normally, the center of pressure was forward of the center gravity just as it left the launch rod, but moved aft as the rocket picked up speed. This is usually not a problem unless it really pitches over and goes into cruise missile mode.

Most likely, failures will fall in the area of recovery system failure; the charge doesn`t go off, insufficient charge, ejection charge at the wrong time, parachute doesn`t come out or doesn`t open.  These problems too can be readily fixed so that everything will work on your next flight.  Examine any recovered hardware for clues as to the cause of the failure, Figure 25-1.   If the nosecone didn`t come off, see if there is evidence the ejection charge went off.   If it did, then the charge was not sufficient or the parachute was packed too tight in the body tube.   If the parachute came out, but didn`t open, then you probably packed it wrong.   Restudy the enclosed video more carefully on how to pack the parachute.   If the charge did not go off, see if the electric match or flashbulb went off. If so, then the powder was not in contact with the bulb or electric match.   Next time, make sure the powder is retained around the bulb or match.   If the bulb or match didn`t go off, then your electronics didn`t work.   Recheck the manufacturers directions to make sure you installed it right.

The bottom line on failures is that you have to do a little digging to find out the cause. Then, just fix it and fly again.

Is It Legal to Make My Own Motors?
Chapter 26

There is a lot of misinformation floating around on making your own motors and this is a major one. Many people will mistakenly tell you it is against the law. The truth is that it is legal to make your own motors without any federal permits or licenses if the motors are not being sold commercially, they are for your own use and you use the motors in the same state you made them. If you are going to start selling rocket motors, then you will need a Bureau of Alcohol, Tobacco and Firearms (ATF) manufacturers permit. If you make a rocket motor for your own use and you want to use it in a different state than the state you made the motor in, you will need an ATF low explosives permit.

It is important to note that none of the chemicals required to make either ammonium nitrate or ammonium perchlorate rocket motors are on the ATF explosives list. You do not need a federal permit to buy these chemicals. However, most suppliers will require that you be a US citizen and be over 18 years of age. While ammonium perchlorate composite propellants is on the ATF explosives list, you do not need a permit if you make the motor for your own use and use it in the same state you made it in. This is true regardless of the amount of propellant.

The next question is, "Does my state have any laws against making motors or require any permits?" Obviously, the answer will vary from state to state. A good place to start would be with the state fire marshal office to determine if there are any laws in your state. If that office doesn't know, you could also try the state attorney general's office. It is important to stress that you are talking about making amateur rocket motors and not fireworks.

If it is permissible in your state, then you need to check with your local government, city and county. A good place to start is with the county fire marshal. They may also be able to give you information on state laws if you were not successful in finding out anything from the state offices. Usually, the main concern from the local fire marshal will be storage of chemicals in your house or garage. In case of a fire at your house, fire fighters will want to know what chemicals might be in the house and where.

Do You Need a Waiver? Launch License?
Chapter 27

In order to fly your rocket, you may need an FAA waiver. If you are planning something big like going into orbit or really high into Space, you will need a launch license from the FAA. If your rocket motor does not use more than 125 grams of propellant and your rocket does not weigh more than 1.5 kilograms, then you do not need a waiver from the FAA to fly. However, you will have the following operating limitations placed on you:

You may not fly your rocket (1) in a manner that creates a collision hazard with other aircraft, (2) at any altitude where clouds or obscuring phenomena of more than 50% coverage prevails, (3) at any altitude where the horizontal visibility is less than five miles, (4) into any cloud and (5) between sunset and sunrise. You will also be required to provide 24 to 48 hour notification before your launch to the FAA air traffic control facility nearest to your launch site. If you are operating within 5 miles of an airport runway or other landing area, you must also provide this information to the manager of the airport. It is important to note, that this is not requesting approval. They cannot stop you from flying. It is simply notification.

The notification must include the following information:

1) Your name and address unless multiple people will be flying. In that case, provide the name and address of the person who will be coordinating the launch.
2) The estimated number of rockets to be flown.
3) The estimated size and weight of each rocket.
4) The estimated highest altitude each rocket will be flown.
5) The location of the launch site.
6) The date, time and duration of the launch.
7) Any other pertinent information requested by the local air traffic control facility.

Most amateurs are going to be over the weight limits and need a waiver. This is not a big deal to obtain. Chapter 28 explains in detail how to fill out the forms and get your waiver.

Launch License

In the 1960's, the United States Government signed an international Space treaty that made the U.S. Government liable for damages caused by any rocket leaving the US or its territories. It also makes the US Government liable for damages from a rocket launched outside the US and its territories if the rocket was made in the United States. This treaty also included many other items about keeping weapons out of Space and so on. At the time, it never occurred to the US Government or any government, that private individuals would ever be making rockets going into Space or orbiting around the earth.

During the 1990`s, it has become very clear, that private citizens or amateurs will be launching rockets into Space. Some have already gone over 37 miles up. Space is considered as starting between 50 and 60 miles above the ground, so amateurs are getting closer and closer. Currently, the US Government has set a limit on the size of amateur rockets. If you go beyond this limit, you will need a launch license from the US Government. The amateur limit states three parameters you cannot exceed on an individual basis. If you exceed any one of them, your rocket is no longer classified as amateur by the Federal Government.

An amateur rocket is defined as a rocket with a total impulse of 200,000 lb-seconds or less and a 15 second burn duration or less and a ballistic coefficient of 12 lb/in2 or less. The ballistic coefficient is defined as the rocket`s gross weight divided by its frontal cross-sectional area. If you are over this limit, then you will need a launch license from the FAA or you can ask for a waiver of the launch license requirement.

What these three parameters really translate into is an altitude straight up for a given drag coefficient and a ballistic range if the rocket is launched as a missile. The US Government has decided that if your rocket doesn`t exceed this limit, most likely you will not do damage to a foreign country`s citizens that the US Government cannot handle. Of course, the governments of Canada, Mexico and Cuba may take different view of all this should an amateur rocket land on their shores.

Suppose you have big dreams of exceeding this limit because you want to put something into orbit. Your best bet is to try to get a Government contract to pursue your work and launch under the umbrella of the US Government. If this is not appealing to you, then the next best bet is to ask for a launch license waiver. This is probably a real long shot for a new rocket or launch vehicle trying to put a payload into orbit. What about getting the license? Well, unless you have a lot of money laying around, forget it. Why? First, you will be required to launch from an FAA approved commercial Spaceport like Cape Canaveral, Vandenberg, White Sands, Wallops, etc. Do you hear the cash register starting to ring? Then, your launch support crew must be certified professionals by the FAA. Care to guess what these guys charge per hour? Then, you will be required to take out a multi-million dollar insurance policy for any damages from your launch, rocket and payload. Want to guess what the premium is for that policy? Ok, by now you should be getting the picture. Once you get a launch license, by definition of the FAA, you are no longer an amateur and you will pay full fare for traveling from amateur to professional ranks.

However, not all is so bleak. I believe in the future, the Government will relax the limit some. More and more rocket launches are being conducted safely in the US and the FAA controllers are getting more used to handling air traffic and rocket traffic. Also, no one has yet bumped up against the amateur limit.   Remember, a rocket with a thrust of 20,000 lbs and a duration of 10 seconds and a total lift off weight of 3,400 lbs and 19 inches in diameter is legally an amateur rocket. It doesn`t require a launch license to fly it.   Such a rocket would indeed be a challenge for an amateur to fly successfully and be one heck of a flight.

Getting an FAA Waiver
Chapter 28

Ok, you`ve looked at the criteria in the last chapter and you need a waiver. It`s no big deal to file the waiver form. Under the current rules, you are supposed to file the waiver with your regional FAA office. A copy of the policy letter from the FAA is included as the last page of this chapter. If after reviewing your waiver, the answer to any of the following four questions is yes, then your waiver will be forwarded to the Air Traffic Airspace and Rules Division in Washington, D.C. for review. The questions are as follows:

Does your waiver:

1) Have a motor or combination of motors, with a total impulse of 200,000 lb-seconds or more; and

2) Have a motor or combination of motors, with a total burning time or operating time of more than 15 seconds (see exception below); and

3) Have a ballistic coefficient (i.e., gross weight in pounds divided by frontal area of the rocket vehicle in square inches) more than 12 pounds per square inch; and

4) Regardless of the answers to questions 1 through 3, have a rocket that will exceed 25,000 ft above ground level.

Exception: If a launch is to take place at a Tripoli Rocket Association-sanctioned event, the 15 second burn time provision does not apply. Such launches may involve rockets that have a motor, or combination of motors, that have a total burning time or operating time of 60 seconds.

Filling out the Waiver Form

Ok, you are ready to fill out the waiver form and send it in. Included with this book is a blank waiver form, which you can copy, and use. Most of it you will not have to fill out, as it is oriented towards aircraft and air shows. A sample waiver form already filled out is shown in Appendix D. Here`s what to put in each block:

Block 1: List your club`s name. If you are flying alone, you can just make up a club name. Don`t use the words like militia in your club`s name.

Block 2: Put your name here.

Block 3: Your mailing address and phone number you can be reached at during the day.

Block 4: List: 101.23 (b). Also, list 101.23(c) if you will be within five miles of an airport.

Block 5: Let's suppose you want a standing altitude to 10,000 ft above ground level with a window to 18,000 ft above ground level. Above ground level can be abbreviated as AGL. Write the following: Normal operation of model rockets weighing more than 1500 grams and containing more than 125 grams of propellant not to exceed 10,000 AGL, with a high altitude window of 18,000 ft, between 0800 MST and 1000 MST.

You will also need to answer those four questions we talked about earlier in this chapter. We have already indicated that we will not be exceeding 25,000 AGL, but we need to answer those other three questions. In our case, we will be under the limits so write the following: All rockets will be below 200,000 lb-sec and 15 second burn duration and 12 lb/in2 ballistic coefficient.

Block 6: You describe the site location and how big it is. The location is usually given as a radial from the VOR and a distance. The VOR is at the center of the Victor airway intersections on your sectional map. Show how big the launch site is in terms of the radius in nautical miles around the launch pad location. Suppose the center of our launch site on the 218o compass radial from the VOR know as Muddy Mountain on the sectional map. We want the airspace in a 3 nautical mile radius around our launch pad. We would write in Block 6 the following: Directly above and within a 3 nautical mile radius of the launch site at 56 statue miles on a 218o radial from Muddy Mountain VOR.

Block 7: List the date you wish to launch and the starting and stopping time of your launch activities. Give yourself plenty of time for setting up, delays and launching. You will have to give your launch times in military time for your local time zone. You will have to convert your local time to military 24-hour time. For military time, 0 is midnight, 1200 hours is noon, 1pm is 1300 hours, 5 p.m. is 1700 hours and so on. Suppose you want to start at 8am and finish at 5pm, Eastern Standard Time. Your times converted to military time would be 0800 and 1700 hours. So you would write: 0800 EST and 1700 EST.

Blocks 8 - 14: Mark as N/A.

Block 15: Sign and date your waiver form.

Remarks Section: Put in the following: Operations will be in accordance with FAA safety codes. All rockets will have recovery devices for a soft landing. 24-48 hour notice will be given to FAA before use of waiver. Notice will be given to FAA when operations have stopped. Map and safety code are attached.

Attach a copy of your safety code and a map showing the launch site. You can use the safety code included in this book or make up your own. I would recommend that the map of the launch site be part of the sectional map. Make an 8-1/2" x 11" copy of the part of the map showing the VOR radial and the launch site. It can be reduced, if necessary.

Now, make four copies of the whole package. Keep one copy of the package for your records and send three copies of the package to the regional FAA office for your area listed in Appendix C.

When your waiver is approved, you will be sent a copy of the waiver and any restrictions they have placed on it. You will also be instructed on any additional things that you might have to do for your launch. When you launch, make sure you have a copy of the approved waiver with you. This will be helpful should some good citizen show up who thinks you are setting up to shoot down planes. Some nosy law enforcement officer might also show up. If you have permission to use the land and have your FAA waiver with you, you can tell these people to Blow it out their pants if they don`t like it.

Stay Alive and In One Piece!
Chapter 29

It`s somewhat obvious, but it needs stating here. It`s not much fun to do amateur rocketry if you are going to blow some part of your body off or burn yourself. In the 1950`s through the 1970`s, amateur rocketry was characterized by the basement bombers. The use of black powder and zinc/sulfur was dangerous and accidents were bound to happen. With the use of composite propellants, those types of accidents should not happen. The two dangers you will face are fire and explosion. These propellants burn at temperatures ranging from 3000o F to 5800o F. That`s hotter than the heating element on your stove when its glowing red hot on high. How would you like to grab a hold of that? When you are mixing, casting or generally working with composite propellant be aware of ignition sources. The propellant will not explode, but if it ignites when you don`t expect it, you could receive a burn.

When you work with the chemicals, be careful of ignition sources or materials that react with them. Both ammonium nitrate and ammonium perchlorate are extremely reactive with powder metals when they are not in a binder. Make sure you do not mix powder metals and these oxidizers together in a dry mix. It will burn explosively if ignited. Magnesium powder when wet will react with the water, releasing hydrogen gas. Hydrogen gas is easily ignited and will explode with unbelievable force. A spoonful of magnesium powder put into water will release enough hydrogen gas to make an explosion equivalent to a very large firecracker. If you follow the propellant mixing directions in this book and clean up spilled chemicals, you should not have any problems.

Don`t work in your basement. First, there is not enough ventilation and second if there is a fire, you will start your whole house on fire. Work in an area that is well ventilated and where a fire will not burn down your house and can quickly be brought under control.

Always wear protective glasses or face shield. Wear clothing that does not build up static electricity and periodically ground yourself out to make sure you are not building up a static charge.

Static firing rocket motors is dangerous. Although the design may be sound, there could be a production flaw that will cause a burn though or weaken a part so that it fails. Burn throughs are not much of a safety problem as flame just shoots through some part of the motor. Structural failure of a part is another story. These parts can shoot through the air at speeds that make them as lethal as a rifle bullet. Never stand in the line of fire of nozzles and bulkheads. Always have a protective barrier between you and any motor you are static firing.

When you are flying your rockets, be ready for it to go unstable and start to do a sky writing routine in the sky. A rocket under power heading right for your nose is a thrill you don't really want to experience. Always have a spot you can dive to so that you can put some barrier between you and the rocket. It can be your car, truck, tree, building, ditch or whatever. Just don't stand in the middle of a flat field with no protective barrier to get behind.

Never try to catch a rocket that is coming down on a parachute. It is coming in much faster than it looks and can really nail you good. Needless to say, you will not try to catch one that is in free fall after the parachute didn't open.

I'm not trying to scare the pants off you. It is not that dangerous to make and fly your amateur rockets. Just use common sense, give the chemicals, propellants, motors, and rockets the respect they deserve. Like firearms, they can be extremely safe or dangerous, depending on who is using them. Always assume the worse could happen at any moment and protect yourself from it.

Personal Comments from the Author
Chapter 30

This is the chapter where I get to make some editorial comments without trying to disguise it as technical material. The first edition of "How To Make Amateur Rockets" was really inspired by the first three booklets we printed in 1994. The first edition book was published in 1996 and was a great success. It turned out to be the classic reference book we had hoped for. Since that time, we have advanced amateur rocketry technology to make it even easier to make your own motors and rockets. I thought it was finally time to incorporate those advances into a second edition.

Figure 30-1: Rocket Camp Students - Course 2

Amateur rocketry has come a long way from when I first wrote the original booklets in 1994. At that time, amateur rocketry was still done by a small group of individuals. Now, there are thousands of amateurs around the world making their own motors and rockets. Many middle schools and high schools in the United States are reintroducing amateur rocketry to their students using this bookset. We also started a Rocket Camp for students based on this book, Figure 30-1.

I have heard from many of you on how you were successfully making motors, experimenting with different propellant formulations and motor designs. All I can say is keep those emails, letters and phone calls coming in. It is really nice to hear from you.

For those of you who are just starting, you must experience the thrill of launching a rocket and motor that you have designed and built from scratch, it cannot be described. You will be floating on air after each successful launch. It will be the same feeling of achievement and pride that has been felt by the designers of Redstone, Atlas, Thor, Saturn V and the Space Shuttle when they watched their rockets roar into Space.

Over the years, I've received a lot of personal criticism from those in high power and sport rocketry. I've gotten comments like, "You're going to ruin it for everybody by promoting Amateur

Rocketry" and "The government is going to shut everybody down because of you". This was usually said with the distinct tone of someone who looks down on amateurs as crackpots, pyromaniacs and the classic basement bomber. You may run into these attitudes, too. If you go onto some the Internet rocketry discussion groups, you will get yourself flamed big time by asking about making your own motors. You will be told it's illegal; you will kill yourself and destroy model and high power rocketry. Don't waste your time with these people. They are just ignorant of current amateur motor technology and how safe it is. They also are not interested in eliminating this ignorance.

Amateur rocketry is at the top of the heap and amateur rocketeers are the elite. You don't have the luxury of blaming a kit designer or a motor manufacturer for failure. Your rocket flies or crashes strictly on your knowledge and skills. If you don't have what it takes, neither will your rocket or its motor. I've given you the basic knowledge to be successful. Quoting Dr. Robert Schuller, *"If you can dream it .... You can do it!"* You've dreamed of making your own rockets and motors, that's why you bought this book. Now, it's time to do it!

Let me be the first to welcome you to this elite and very special group ... *amateur rocketeers!*

Some Motor Designs to Get You Started
Appendix A

We have included some motor designs using PVC pipe and fittings to help get you started in designing and building your own motors. None of the motors have exit cones, just straight hole nozzles. All the motors use the same propellant formulation of 20% magnesium, 20% R20LM binder, 60% ammonium nitrate. The particle size for the magnesium is approximately -650 mesh sold by Pyrotek as -650 or 1000 mesh.

For more motor designs go to: **www.space-rockets.com/motor.html**

1.25" PVC Motor

This is a nice motor that is simple to make. If you have not made your own motors before, I highly recommend you start with this one. These motors can be made to fit in 54 mm motor mounts with tape wrapped around the PVC fittings.

Motor Specifications - Version 1

- Chamber is 1.25 inch PVC pipe Schedule 40
- 6 Propellant Cartridges Cast into 1 inch PVC pipe
- Cartridge length = 1.75 inches
- Cartridge Diameter = 1.05 inch
- Bore Diameter = 3/8 inch
- Throat Diameter = 1/4 inch
- Nozzle = PVC threaded fitting with Durham's Water Putty cast into thread end of fitting. Use a graphite insert with Water Putty or just Water Putty for the nozzle.
- Delay Length = approx. 1/2 inches
- Propellant Weight = 0.417 lbs = 190 grams

To assemble the motor, fill the 1 inch PVC pipe propellant sleeves and delay tube with propellant and let them completely cure. When they have cured, drill out the 3/8 inch bore in each cartridge using a drill bit that you turn with your fingers or an electric drill at a very low speed. Try to keep the bore going down the center of the cartridge.

Drill out the water putty in the PVC fitting for the 1/4 inch throat. There is no need to make an entrance region or exit cone on the nozzle. A straight hole will do. Glue the PVC end cap with the delay onto the PVC pipe using primer and PVC cement. Put in the six propellant cartridges.   If you cut the PVC pipe right, the end of the last cartridge should just be a little short of the end of the pipe.   Glue the nozzle onto the pipe using primer and PVC cement.   Let the cement dry.   The motor is now done and ready for use.

If you use the graphite insert in the nozzle, the average thrust will be almost 16 lbs for about 3.5 seconds. If you use just Water Putty for the nozzle, the thrust will be regressive rather than neutral with an average thrust of 10 lbs and a burn duration of about 4.5 seconds.

Here is a lower power version with a regressive thrust - time curve. It has an intial thrust of about 8 lbs and burns for about 6 seconds. Average thrust is about 6 lbs.

Motor Specifications - Version 2

- Chamber is 1.25 inch PVC pipe Schedule 40
- 5 Propellant Cartridges Cast into 1 inch PVC pipe
- Cartridge length = 1.5 inches
- Bore Diameter = 7/16 inch
- Throat Diameter = 1/4 inch
- Nozzle = PVC threaded fitting with Durham's Water Putty cast into thread end of fitting.
- Delay Length = approx. 1/2 inches
- Propellant Weight = 0.282 lbs = 128 grams

2 Inch PVC Pipe Motor

This motor is in the J class range and is a good second motor to make. You will need 2 inch PVC pipe for the motor case and 1.5 inch PVC pipe for the propellant cartridges.   You do not need rubber insulation inside the 2 inch PVC pipe.   This motor is use in Course 2 of The Rocket Camp.

Motor Specifications - Version 1

- Chamber is 2 inch PVC pipe Schedule 40
- 7 Propellant Cartridges Cast into 1.5 inch PVC pipe schedule 40
- Cartridge length = 2 inches
- Cartridge Diameter = 1 inch
- Bore Diameter = 5/8 inch
- Throat Diameter = 3/8 inch
- Nozzle = Graphite insert inside a PVC fitting filled with Durham's Water Putty
- Delay Length = approx. 3/4 inches
- Propellant Weight = 1.03 lbs

Another good motor to make uses a CE phenolic insert for the throat material and has a little higher impulse.

Motor Specifications - Version 2

- Chamber is 2 inch PVC pipe Schedule 40
- 5 Propellant Cartridges Cast into 1.5 inch PVC pipe schedule 40
- Cartridge length = 4 inches
- Bore Diameter = 5/8 inch
- Throat Diameter = 3/8 inch
- Nozzle = CE phenolic insert inside a PVC fitting filled with Durham's Water Putty
- Delay Length = approx. 3/4 inches
- Propellant Weight = 1.48 lbs

3 Inch PVC Pipe Motor

The 3" PVC pipe motors can be made using 2.5 inch PVC pipe for the propellant cartridges. You can use either graphite for the throat insert or CE phenolic for the throat insert. If you use graphite, it will be a higher thrust motor. The CE phenolic will be a high initial thrust and then regressive.

Motor Specifications

- Chamber is 3 inch PVC pipe Schedule 40
- 5 Propellant Cartridges Cast into 2.5 inch PVC pipe schedule 40
- Cartridge length = 4 inches
- Bore Diameter = 1.5 inch
- Throat Diameter = 5/8 inch
- Nozzle = Graphite or CE phenolic insert inside a PVC fitting filled with Durham's Water Putty
- Propellant Weight = 3.21 lbs

4 Inch PVC Pipe Motor

There are two basic variations of this motor depending on whether you can get 3.5 inch diameter PVC pipe. It is difficult to find, but it is available in some places. If you use the 3.5 inch PVC pipe for the propellant cartridges, you will not need to insulate the 4 inch PVC pipe. If you use 3" PVC pipe for the propellant cartridges, you will need to put a sheet of 1/16 inch rubber inside the 4 inch PVC pipe. You may actually want to double the insulation thickness as the motor will get very warm after the firing with only a 1/16" thick sheet of rubber. You can use either graphite or CE phenolic for the throat insert. The graphite will make a stronger motor.

Motor Specifications - Version 1 (3.5" PVC Cartridges)

- Chamber is 4 inch PVC pipe (Schedule 40)
- 4 Propellant Cartridges Cast into 3.5 inch PVC pipe schedule 40
- Cartridge length = 5 inches
- Bore Diameter = 2.50 inches
- Throat Diameter = 3/4 inch
- Nozzle = Graphite or CE phenolic inside a PVC fitting filled with Durham's Water Putty
- Propellant Weight = 4.82 lbs

Motor Specifications - Version 2 (3.0" PVC Cartridges)

- Chamber is 4 inch PVC pipe (Schedule 40)
- 7 Propellant Cartridges Cast into 3.0 inch PVC pipe schedule 40
- Cartridge length = 3 inches
- Bore Diameter = 2.00 inches
- Throat Diameter = 3/4 inch
- Chamber must be insulated with rubber
- Nozzle = Graphite or CE phenolic inside a PVC fitting filled with Durham's Water Putty
- Propellant Weight = 4.21 lbs

Sample Safety Code for Launches

Appendix B

<u>FORWARD</u>

The following are guidelines meant to allow you to enjoy Amateur Rocketry and to encourage safe and constructive involvement in it. Realize that no Safety Code can assure 100% safety this is up!

1.0   ROCKET MOTORS:

1.1   Commercial custom motors and experimental motors may be used at all launches, without being listed on the Certified Motor List.

1.2   All rocket motors will be electrically ignited.

2.0   ROCKETS:

2.1   Rockets will be built as light as possible for the intended purpose of the rocket.

2.2   Rockets will have a suitable means for providing stabilizing and restoring forces necessary to maintain a substantially true and predictable upward flight path.

2.3   Rockets shall be constructed so as to be capable of more than one flight. It will be provided with means for a slow and safe descent. If a rocket is to descend in more than one part, then the parts should have means for a slow and safe descent.

2.4   Any equipment, devices, or material which relies upon flammable, smoldering, or otherwise combustible substances, which are not a motor, shall be designed, built, and implemented or otherwise used in a manner which will minimize the possibility of a fire after launch.

3.0   LAUNCH PLATFORMS AND IGNITION SYSTEMS:

3.1   A launching device, or mechanism, must be used which is sufficiently rigid and of sufficient length to guarantee that the rocket shall be independently stable when it leaves the device. This launching device shall be sufficiently stable on the ground to prevent significant shifts from the planned launch angle, or the accidental triggering of any first-motion ignition devices.

3.2   A launch angle of less than 15 degrees from the vertical must be used when flying rockets.

3.3   Any and all ignition systems on rockets must be remotely and electrically activated.

3.4   The launch of any rocket must be completely under the control of the person launching it. When flying alone, the individual person is responsible for range safety, and launch control safety. When flying at an Amateur Rocket Society of America sponsored meet, the Range Safety Office (RSO) will turn over control of the launch, for the duration of the countdown, to the designated Launch Control Officer (LCO) when the launching range is deemed safe to launch.

3.5   The launch system firing circuit must return to the off position when released (if a mechanical launch system is used) or reset (if an electronic launch system is used).

3.6   Excessive lengths of fuse, or complex pyrotechnical ignition arrangements should be avoided. The simplest and most direct ignition trains are encouraged to promote range safety.

3.7   Igniters should be installed at the last practical moment, and once installed, electrical igniter wires should be shorted and/or pyrotechnical systems mechanically protected to prevent premature ignition from EMI or heat sources.

4.0   FLYING FIELDS AND CONDITIONS:

4.1   All launches of rockets must be conducted in compliance with Federal, State, and Local law.

4.2   Rocket flights must be made only when weather conditions permit the average person to visually observe the entire flight of the rocket from lift-off to the deployment of the recovery system. It is recommended that no rockets be launched when winds exceed 20 miles per hour.

4.3   No rocket shall contain en explosive warhead type device, nor will they be launched at targets on the ground.

4.4   An amateur rocket flying field must be equipped with an appropriately rated fire-extinguishing device. Each launch pad should have a water container within 10 feet of the pad. A well-stocked First Aid kit and a person, familiar with their use is recommended.

4.5   Advanced Rockets shall be launched from a clear area, free of any easy to burn materials, and away from buildings, power lines, tall trees, or flying aircraft. The flying field must be of sufficient size to permit recovery of a given rocket within its confines.

4.6   At no time shall recovery of a rocket from power lines, or other dangerous places, be attempted. Any rocket that becomes entangled in a utility line (power, phone, etc.) is a hazard to the utility line and untrained persons who may be attracted to it. The owner of the vehicle will make every effort to contact the proper utility company and have their trained personnel remove it.

4.7   No rocket shall be caught during descent.

4.8   All persons in the vicinity of any launches must be advised that a launching is imminent before a rocket may be ignited and launched. A minimum five-second countdown must be given immediately prior to ignition and launch of a rocket.

4.9   A spectator line will be established parallel with the launch controller's table. Launch pads for motors exceeding J class, or clusters of G, H, and/or I's shall be set 200 feet from the spectator line.

FAA Regional Offices

Appendix C

The following are the FAA Regional Offices for the United States. If your launch site is in the following states, you will be under the jurisdiction of these regional offices.

<u>CT, MA, VT, RI, NH, ME:</u>

FAA-ANE
New England Region
12 New England Executive Park
Burlington, MA 01803-5299
(781) 238-7520

<u>NY, NJ, DE, MD,DC,PA, VA, WV:</u>

FAA-AEA
Eastern Region
Fitzgerald Federal Bldg.
JFK International Airport
Jamaica, NY 11430
(718) 553-2616

<u>AL, FL, GA, MS, KY, NC, SC, TN:</u>

FAA-ASO
Southern Region
P.O. Box 20636
Atlanta, GA 30320
(404) 305-5585

IL, MI, WI, MN, OH, ND, SD:

FAA-AGL
Great Lakes Region
2300 East Devon Avenue
Des Plains, IL 60018
(847) 294-7568

IA, KS, MO, NE:

FAA-ACE
Central Region
601 East 12th Street
Kansas City, MO 64106
(816) 426-3408 (MO & KS) and (816) 426-3409 (IA & NE)

AR, LA, OK, TX:

FAA-ASW
Southwest Region
2601 Meacham Blvd.
Ft. Worth, TX 76193-0520
(817) 222-5520

WA, OR, ID, MT, WY, CO, UT:

FAA-ANM
Northwest Mountain Region
1601 Lind Avenue, SW
Renton, WA 98055-4056
(425) 227-2520

CA, AZ, NV, HI:

FAA-AWP
Western Pacific Region
15000 Aviation Bld.
Hawthorne, CA 90260
(310) 725-6605

AK:

FAA-AAL
Alaska Region
222 West 7th Avenue
Anchorage, AK 99513-7587
(907) 271-5893

High Plains Rocket Society
4010A South Poplar, #23
Casper, WY 82601

July 1, 1999

FAA Northwest Mountain Region
Attn: Air Traffic Division - Air Space Branch
1601 Lind Avenue, SW
Renton, WA 98055-4056

    I have enclosed with this letter our waiver application to fly rockets on September 9, 1999. We have permission from the federal Bureau of Land Management to use the land for the purpose of launching model rockets. Our group will also have a cellular phone on-site. Please call me at (307) 265-5895 (9am-5pm weekdays), if you have any questions.

                Sincerely,

                John H. Wickman
                High Plains Rocket Society

No certificate may be issued unless a completed application
form has been received (14 C.F.R. 91, 101, and 105).

U.S. Department of Transportation

Federal Aviation Administration

APPLICATION FOR
CERTIFICATE OF WAIVER
OR AUTHORIZATION

Form Approved: O.M.B. No. 2120-0027

APPLICANTS — DO NOT USE THESE SPACES	
Region	Date

Action

☐ Approved   ☐ Disapproved — *Explain under "Remarks"*

Signature of authorized FAA representative

INSTRUCTIONS

Submit this application in triplicate (3) to any FAA Flight Standards district office.

Applicants requesting a Certificate of Waiver or Authorization for an aviation event must complete all the applicable items on this form and attach a properly marked 7.5 series Topographic Quadrangle Map(s), published by the U.S. Geological Survey (scale 1:24,000), of the proposed operating area. The map(s) must include scale depictions of the flightlines, showlines, race courses, and the location of the air event control point, Police dispatch, ambulance, and fire

fighting equipment. The applicant may also wish to submit photographs and scale diagrams as supplemental material to assist in the FAA's evaluation of a particular site. Application for a Certificate of Waiver or Authorization must be submitted 45 days prior to the requested date of the event.

Applicants requesting a Certificate of Waiver or Authorization for activities other than an aviation event will complete items 1 through 8 only and the certification, item 15, on the reverse.

1. Name of organization

High Plains Rocket Society

2. Name of responsible person

John Wickman

3. Permanent mailing address

House number and street or route number	City	State and ZIP code	Telephone No.
4010A South Poplar #23	Casper	WY 82601	(307) 265-5895

4. FAR section and number to be waived

101.23 (b)

5. Detailed description of proposed operation *(Attach supplement if needed)*

Normal operation of model rockets weighing more than 1500 grams and containing more than 125 grams of propellant not to exceed 10,000 AGL, with a high altitude window of 18,000 ft between 0800 MST and 1000 MST. All rockets will be below 200,000 lb-sec and 15 second burn duration and 12 lb/in² ballistic coefficient

6. Area of operation *(Location, altitudes, etc.)*

Directly above and within a 3 nautical mile radius of the launch site at 56 statue miles on a 218° radial from Muddy Mountain VOR.

7a. Beginning *(Date and hour)*

September 9, 1999; 0800 Hours MST

b. Ending *(Date and hour)*

September 9/99, 1700 hours MST

8.

Aircraft make and model (a)	Pilot's Name (b)	Certificate number and rating (c)	Home address (Street, City, State) (d)
N/A	N/A	N/A	N/A

D-2

9. The air event will be sponsored by:

10. Permanent mailing address	House number and street or route number	City	State and ZIP code	Telephone No.

11. Policing (Describe provisions to be made for policing the event.)

12. Emergency facilities (Mark all that will be available at time and place of air event.)

☐ Physician   ☐ Fire truck   ☐ Other — Specify _____

☐ Ambulance   ☐ Crash wagon   _____

13. Air Traffic control (Describe method of controlling traffic, including provision for arrival and departure of scheduled aircraft.)

14. Schedule of Events   (Include arrival and departure of scheduled aircraft and other periods the airport may be open.)

Hour (a)	Date (b)	Event (c)

If sufficient space is not available, the entire schedule of events may be submitted on separate sheets, in the order and manner indicated above.

Please Read > The undersigned applicant accepts full responsibility for the strict observance of the terms of the Certificate of Waiver or Authorization, and understands that the authorization contained in such certificate will be strictly limited to the above described operation.

15. Certification — I CERTIFY that the foregoing statements are true.

Date	Signature of applicant
July 1, 1999	*[signature]*

Remarks
Operations will be accordance with FAA safety codes. All rockets will have recovery devices for a soft landing. 24-48 hour notice will be given to FAA, before use of waiver. Notice will be given to FAA when operations have stopped. Map and safety code are attached.

FAA Form 7711-2 (6-86) Supersedes Previous Edition

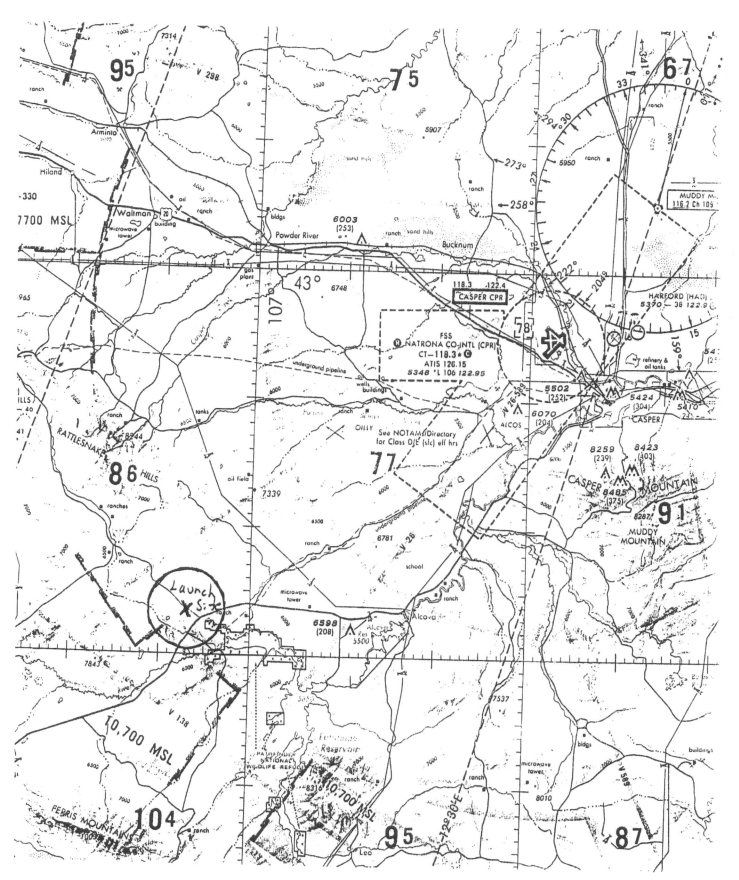

D-4

HIGH PLAINS ROCKET SOCIETY
SAFETY CODE

FORWARD

The following are guidelines and are meant as a means to allow you to enjoy Advanced Rocketry, not to stifle creativity, but to encourage safe and constructive involvement in rocketry with the maximum of enjoyment and participation. Realize that with Advanced Rocketry no Safety Code we adopt can assure safety as much as would be desired, this is up to you the member!

1. ROCKET MOTORS:

1.1 Members may use NAR or Tripoli certified manufactured motors at all launches.

1.2 Commercial custom motors and experimental motors, may be used at all launches, without being listed on the Certified Motor List, provided the manufacturer supplies proof of satisfactory static tests.

1.3 All rocket motors will be electrically ignited.

2. ADVANCED ROCKET VEHICLES:

2.1 Advanced Rockets will be built as light as possible for the intended purpose of the rocket. The use of metal will not be permitted in the nose cone, airframe, motor mount, or fins of an Advanced Rocket.

2.2 An Advanced Rocket will have a suitable means for providing stabilizing and restoring forces necessary to maintain a substantially true and predictable upward flight path.

2.3 An Advanced Rocket shall be constructed so as to be capable of more than one flight. It will be provided with means for a slow and safe descent. If a rocket is to descend in more than one part, then the parts should have means for a slow and safe descent.

2.4 Any equipment, devices, or material which relies upon flammable, smoldering, or otherwise combustible substances, which are not a motor, shall be designed, built, and implemented, or otherwise used in a manner which will minimize the possibility of a fire after launch.

3. LAUNCH PLATFORMS AND IGNITION SYSTEMS:

3.1 A launching device, or mechanism, must be used which is sufficiently rigid and of sufficient length to guarantee that the rocket shall be independently stable when it leaves the device. This launching device shall be sufficiently stable on the ground to prevent significant shifts from the planned launch angle, or the accidental triggering of any first-motion ignition devices.

3.2 The launch pad, or device, shall have a blast deflector sufficient to prevent damage, or fire hazard, to surrounding equipment (including the launch pad itself), or the surrounding area.

3.3 A launch angle of less than *15* degrees from the vertical must be used when flying Advanced Rockets.

3.4 Any and all ignition systems on Advanced Rockets must be remotely and electrically activated.

3.5 The launch of any rocket must be completely under the control of the person launching it. When flying alone, the individual person is responsible for range safety, and launch control safety. When flying at a High Plains Rocket Society sponsored meet, the Range Safety Officer (RSO), in control of the launch range, must be present. The RSO will turn over control of the launch, for the duration of the countdown, to the designated Launch Control Officer (LCO) when the launching range is deemed safe to launch.

3.6 Minimum requirements for the RSO are (a) membership in good standing and (b) Advanced Rocketry experience, similar or equal to that expected at a particular launch.

3.7 The launch system firing circuit must return to the off position when released (if a mechanical launch system is used) or reset (if an electronic launch system is used). A permissive circuit controlled by the RSO at all times and capable of releasing the firing circuit is advisable.

3.8 Excessive lengths of fuse, or complex pyrotechnical ignition arrangements should be avoided. The simplest and most direct ignition trains are encouraged to promote range safety.

3.9 Igniters should be installed at the last practical moment, and once installed, electrical igniter wires should be shorted and/or pyrotechnical systems mechanically protected to prevent premature ignition from EMI or heat sources.

4. FLYING FIELDS AND CONDITIONS:

4.1 All launches of Advanced Rocket Vehicles must be conducted in compliance with Federal, State, and Local law.

4.2 Rocket flights must be made only when weather conditions permit the average person to visually observe the entire flight of the rocket from lift-off to the deployment of the recovery system. No Advanced Rockets will be launched when winds exceed 20 miles per hour.

4.3 No Advanced Rocket shall contain an explosive warhead type device, nor will they be launched at targets on the ground.

4.4 An Advanced Rocket flying field must be equipped with an appropriately rated fire extinguishing device. Each launch pad must have a five gallon container filled with water within 10 feet of the pad. A well stocked First Aid kit, and a person, or persons, familiar with their use must be present.

4.5 Advanced Rockets shall be launched from a clear area, free of any easy to burn materials, and away from buildings, power lines, tall trees, or flying aircraft. The flying field must be of sufficient size to permit recovery of a given rocket within its confines.

4.6 At no time shall recovery of an Advanced Rocket vehicle from power lines, or other dangerous places, be attempted. Any rocket that becomes entangled in a utility line (power, phone, etc.) is a hazard to the utility line and untrained persons who may be attracted to it. The owner of the vehicle will make every effort to contact the proper utility company and have their trained personnel remove it.

4.7 No Advanced Rocket shall be caught during descent.

4.8 All persons in the vicinity of any launches must be advised that a launching is imminent before a rocket may be ignited and launched. A minimum five second countdown must be given immediately prior to ignition and launch of a rocket.

4.9 All launch pads will not be located within 1,500 feet of any permanent structures. A spectator line will be established parallel with the launch controller's table. No vehicles will be parked within 50 feet of the spectator line. Launch pads for motors exceeding J class, or clusters of G, H, and/or I's shall be set 200 feet from the spectator line.

4.10 No one will be permitted to sit within the area between the parked vehicle line and the spectator line, other than the RSO, LCO, and designated assistant(s) at the launch control table.

4.11 No one will be permitted in the launch area between the LCO table and the launch pads except vehicle crew for prepping purposes. Crew photographers, or event photographers, permitted in the launch area will maintain a safe distance from the launch pad and out of the way of vehicle crews.

4.12 All rockets to be launched must be presented to the RSO for inspection, assignment, and logged into the flight record with the LCO.

NOTE: This Safety Code may and will be altered and/or updated as seen needed the High Plains Rocket Society. Any modifications to this Code must be approved by the membership.

Challenges of Large Solid Rocket Motors

Appendix E

This book has focused on rocket motors and rockets in the range of interest for most amateurs. However, it is possible that you may be contemplating something larger. If you are, I would to point out in this section some technical issues that will become important.

Propellant Strength/Mechanical Properties

If you are going to be making solid rocket motors with diameters approaching a foot with long grain lengths, the structural strength of the propellant becomes important. The propellant will be very heavy and the weight of this propellant will basically be hanging on the layer of propellant against the insulation. Let's suppose you have a motor which is 8 ft long, 12 inches in diameter with a bore of four inches. The propellant weight will be approximately 482 lbs. This weight will have to be supported by the layer of propellant against the internal insulation. If the propellant doesn't have the shear strength, it will tear or crack while the rocket sits on the pad. If the rocket experiences a four g acceleration during lift-off, the shear load on the propellant will increase to 1928 lbs. Should this be too much for the propellant, it will tear during lift-off and the rocket motor will explode due to overpressurization.

For this size of motor, you should test the structural strength of the propellant. The procedures are the same as for any material. You pull it apart and measure the force required for the propellant to fail. You should also do this in shear. With the tensile and shear strength of the propellant, you can use standard stress equations to see if the propellant would fail. I would recommend a trip to the library to get references on these types of calculations. You will probably find out that you will have to cast your propellant under vacuum to get the proper strength.

Propellant/Insulation/Chamber Bonding

The same problem with the strength of the propellant also applies to the bondlines of the propellant to the insulation and the insulation to the chamber. These bondlines must support the same loads from the propellant on the pad and under acceleration. Again, the best approach is to make test samples with different adhesives to see what works best. It is unlikely that just casting propellant into insulation will provide an adequate bond. You will probably have to coat the insulation with an adhesive before casting. I would suggest you do a literature search on adhesives and do your own experiments.

Segmented Propellant Grains

Some amateurs have attempted to scale up segmented grains used in reload motors to larger amateur motors. There are two basic problems with this approach. First, the propellant segments will crush each other on lift-off unless they are bonded to the motor chamber. We can illustrate this by using the previous motor example. Suppose we take our 492 lbs of propellant and make it into six propellant cartridges of 82 lbs each. The bottom cartridge has the weight of the other five cartridges sitting on it. This 410 lbs of load on the bottom cartridge will increase to 1640 lbs under the four g acceleration forces of lift off. Take a propellant cartridge and put 1640 lbs on it and see what happens. Most likely, you will see cracking of the grain. If so, your motor will explode due the increased burning surface area and resultant overpressurization.

The second problem occurs when the propellant cartridges are unrestricted to burning on the ends. What happens during the initial acceleration of the rocket is that the these propellant cartridges are squeezed together. The gap between the propellant cartridges becomes almost non-existent. The gases from the burning propellant between the cartridges can barely escape and the gap acts as a secondary throat for the burning process, Figure E-1. This gap can get so small that the pressure between cartridges can build up to values exceeding the propellant and chamber strength. The result, an explosion shortly after lift-off of the rocket. If you do try a segmented approach, make sure you bond the cartridges to the chamber and leave a gap between cartridges so the gases can escape between them.

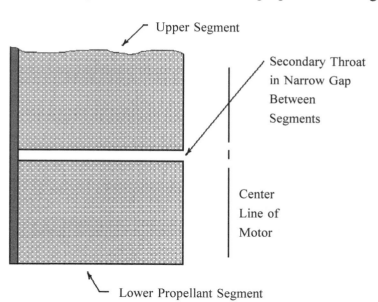

Upper Segment

Secondary Throat in Narrow Gap Between Segments

Center Line of Motor

Lower Propellant Segment

Figure E-1: Secondary Throat Forming Between Burning Propellant Segments in Large Motors

Making Strand Burn Rate Measurements

Appendix F

The real key to making successful amateur rocket motors is knowing the burn rate of your propellant as a function of pressure. Fortunately, the burn rate of composite propellants follows a simple equation:

$$\text{Burn rate} = r = c * P_c^{\,n}$$

If you can get the values for the coefficient, c, and the exponent, n, then you are all set. The trick is getting those values. As mentioned in Chapter 15, you can use static firing data to refine these values, but how do you get them in the first place?

Let's suppose you have come up a great formulation using *CHEM* and have made a few sample batches. The propellant mixes well and seems to ignite easily and burns steady under atmospheric conditions. What do you use for c and n? You could guess values based on a similar propellant, make a motor and hope for the best. A better way would be to make propellant strand burn rate measurements.

In propellant strand tests, you burn strands of propellant at a variety of pressures. From these tests, you know the average pressure and burn rate. You then plot the burn rate versus pressure on $\log_{10}$ vs. $\log_{10}$ paper, use computer software to plot it or make a couple of hand calculations. The idea is to do the tests so that they cover the range of chamber pressures you would expect in your motors. Also, the larger the range of pressure points and the more points, the more accurate your results will be. You will need at least two points to get a line, but I would recommend at least four data points.

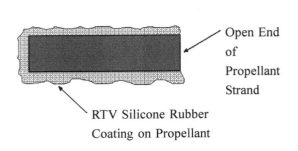

Open End of Propellant Strand

RTV Silicone Rubber Coating on Propellant

Figure F-1: Propellant Strand

To make strand burn rate measurements, you first cut propellant samples into strands or strips. Make the strands one inch long and about 3/8 inches in diameter. It is not important that they be perfectly circular. Coat all sides with RTV silicone rubber except on one end, Figure F-1.

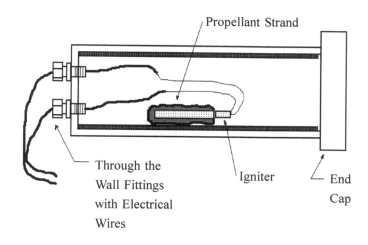

Propellant Strand

Through the Wall Fittings with Electrical Wires

Igniter

End Cap

Figure F-2: Pressure Chamber for Strand Tests

Attach an igniter to the open end of the propellant strand. Insert the propellant strand with the igniter into the pressure chamber, Figure F-2. Attach the igniter wires to the igniter hook-up wires coming from the two fittings. Coat the wires inside the chamber with Plumber's Putty so that they will not get burned up when the propellant strand burns inside the chamber. The putty can be peeled off after the test. Use new putty for each test. The thickness of the coating should be about 1/2 inch. You will find after the firing that the outer layer of the putty is very hard and crusty while the inside is the original softness.

To make the fittings with an electrical wire through it, use standard 1/8 NPT male threaded fittings with a compression fitting on one end. The fittings can be brass or steel. Fill the fitting with Durham's Water Putty and insert a wire through the fitting. Let the putty harden for a few days. The putty will make a seal and keep the wire in the fitting.

The pressure chamber should be attached to a regulated nitrogen bottle as shown in Figure F-3. An on-off valve is between the nitrogen regulator and the pressure chamber and an-other on-off valve on 1/4" tubing is attached to the pressure chamber. A good safety feature is to also attached a pressure relief valve on 1/4" tubing to the pressure chamber. You can buy relief valves which can

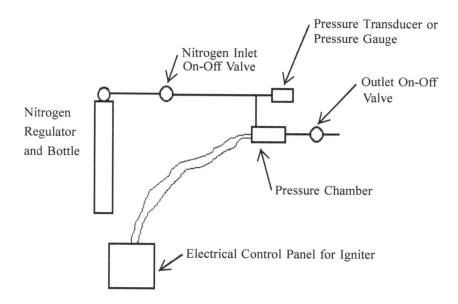

Pressure Transducer or Pressure Gauge

Nitrogen Inlet On-Off Valve

Outlet On-Off Valve

Nitrogen Regulator and Bottle

Pressure Chamber

Electrical Control Panel for Igniter

Figure F-3: Schematic of Strand Propellant Test Equipment

be set to a variety of pressures. If the pressure in the chamber exceeds the relief valve setting, the valve opens and vents the pressure chamber. This venting will continue until the pressure drops below the setting, then the relief valve closes.

You will also need to attach a pressure gauge or pressure transducer to the pressure chamber. A pressure transducer is the best as it can be recorded by your computer to get an accurate pressure versus time record. However, you can use a pressure gauge. In this case, use a camcorder to record the pressure readings.

To run a strand burn rate test, put the propellant strand in the pressure chamber with an igniter and close the chamber. Close the outlet valve on the chamber and open the nitrogen inlet valve. Pressurize the pressure chamber to the desired starting pressure using the nitrogen regulator. Close the nitrogen inlet valve to the pressure chamber. The pressure chamber will now be isolated from the nitrogen bottle so a back flow to the nitrogen regulator cannot happen. Start recording pressure data from the transducer or pressure gauge and energize the igniter. You can use your launch pad electrical system to work the igniter. Make sure you are behind a protective barrier or well away from the chamber when you do the test. After the igniter goes off, you should see a rapid rise by the needle if you are using a pressure gauge. It will be followed by a slow fall off of the needle when the propellant is done burning. After the test, open the outlet valve to bleed off the propellant gas. When the chamber pressure has dropped to zero, you can safely open the chamber.

You should be able to get the nitrogen bottle and regulator from any standard industrial gas supplier. The pressure chamber should be insulated with sheet rubber just like a rocket chamber. The chamber can be metal for higher pressures, but you could also use schedule 80 PVC pipe if all your motors will be using PVC pipe for chambers. Watch out if using PVC pipe as if it explodes it will fragment rather than just split open. It would be smart regardless of chamber material to put a protective shield around the chamber.

A Lower Cost Alternative to Using Nitrogen

The best way to obtain the data is to use nitrogen gas to initially pressurize the chamber. However, the cost of a regulator (about $100 to $150) and rental of a nitrogen cylinder may be too expensive for you. An alternative is to use the propellant strand to do the entire pressurization of the chamber. In this case, the pressure in the chamber always starts at ambient pressure. When the propellant strand ignites, the propellant gases pressurize the chamber. The more propellant, the higher the pressure. The set-up for this type of self pressurization would be the same as shown in Figure F-3, except there would not be a nitrogen line.

One problem with this type of method is that a given strand size more or less gives the same maximum pressure for a given pressure chamber. You can get different pressures by changing the diameter of the strand. Larger diameters will yield higher pressures. Another method is to keep your propellant strands the same size and add chunks of propellant to simply provide pressurization gas. These chunks will be ignited by the igniter along with the propellant strand. If you go to standard chunk sizes, you can add a certain number to obtain a given maximum pressure. You will have to do a little experimentation to find a workable size and number of chunks to obtain a desired pressure.

It is not all a shot in the dark. You can make a fairly good estimate of the maximum pressure for a given propellant formulation. From *CHEM*, you know the flame temperature and molecular weight. With this information and knowing the mass of propellant inside the chamber and the volume of the chamber, you can estimate the maximum chamber pressure. Let's assume the chamber is two inches in diameter and has a length of six inches, then the volume is:

Chamber volume = 0.785 * (Length) * (Diameter)^2

Chamber volume = 0.785 * 6 * (2)^2 = 0.785 * 6 * 4 = 18.84 inch^3

Chamber volume = 18.84 inch^3 = 18.84/1728 = 0.0109 ft^3

From our *CHEM* output, we know that the predicted flame temperature is 3400° F or 3860° R and the molecular weight is 20.76. The equation for calculating the maximum pressure in the strand chamber is:

Max. Chamber Pressure = P_o = (Gas Density) * (Gas Constant) * (Gas Temperature)

This can be rewritten for all the parameters:

P_o (psia) = [(Wt. of Propellant) * 10.73 * (Flame Temp.)]/[(Chamb. Vol.) * (Mole. Wt.)]

where the weight of propellant is in lbs, the flame temperature is in degrees R and chamber volume is in cubic feet. Suppose we have a strand that weighs 0.0015 lbs or 0.68 grams. For our given chamber, we would calculate a maximum pressure as follows:

P_o = (0.0015 * 10.73 * 3860)/(0.0109 * 20.76) = 62.127/0.2263 = 274.5 psia

We would subtract 14.7 from this pressure to obtain the gauge pressure of 259.8 psi or 260 psi. Now, this assumes the gas does not lose temperature to the surrounding walls of the chamber. In reality, it will lose temperature heating the chamber walls so the actual pressure would be less.

Obtaining Burn Rate and Pressure Data from the Test

Assuming you cut all your strands to one inch in length, you can get the burn rate for each test very easily. Determine the time the pressure increased in the chamber and divide that into one inch or one. Let's say we used a pressure gauge and it started out at 100 psi. It then rose to 250 psi in 7 seconds. The pressure rise time would be 7 seconds and we would divide that into one to get 0.143. This would be a burn rate of 0.143 inches per second. To get the average pressure, you just add the starting pressure to the end pressure and divide by two. So, we add 100 psi to 250 psi to get 350 psi and then divide by two to get 175 psi. So our one data point is a burn rate of 0.143 inches per second at a pressure of 175 psi.

How to Get the Burn Rate Parameters from the Data

You made a series of tests and now you have a table of burn rate versus pressure. Let's say that Table F-1 represents your data. Now, if you can find log-log paper, you can plot your pressure and burn rate data directly on the paper. However, if you cannot find this paper, you can take the log of the pressures and burn rates and plot that on regular graph paper. We've shown the log values in Table F-1 so you can be sure you are getting the correct values. It is the log of the values, *not the ln of the values.* Look for the LOG button on your calculator.

Sample Data From Strand Burn Rate Tests

Table F-1

Pressure (psi)	Burn Rate (Inch/Second)	Log Pressure	Log Burn Rate
100	0.055	2.000	-1.260
150	0.063	2.176	-1.201
250	0.073	2.398	-1.137
500	0.100	2.699	-1.000
750	0.120	2.875	-0.921

If you plot the log of the data, you will get something like that shown in Figure F-4. The

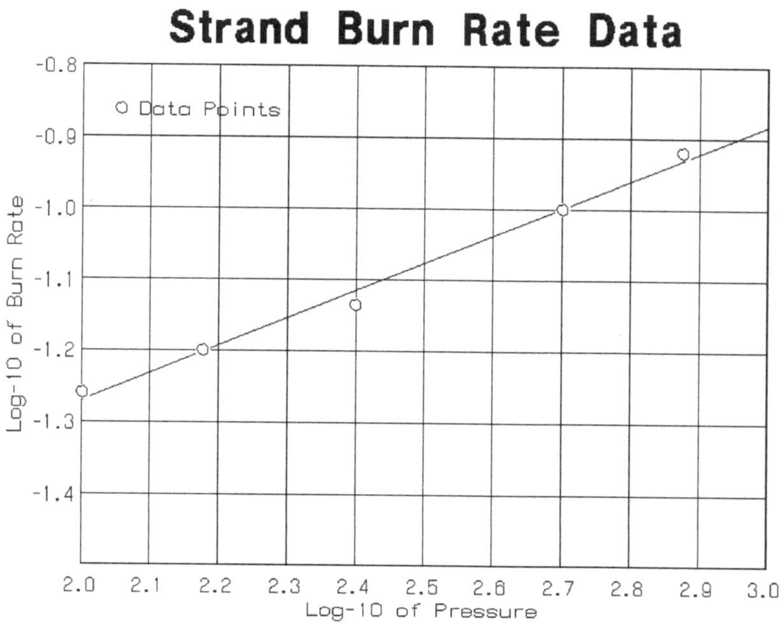

Strand Burn Rate Data

Figure F-4: Plot of Strand Burn Rate Data

burn rate equation will be a straight line on a log-log graph. In this case, the best fit of the data is the line shown in the figure. That line is the burn rate equation for the propellant formulation tested in the strand burn rate equipment. Don't worry that all the data points are not on the line. You may have a case where none of them fall on a line. The point is to draw a line that best fits or comes the closest to all the data points.

Ok, we have the line. How do we translate that to the values for c and n. Well, the slope of the line is n. We can calculate that first. The slope of the line is the rise of the line over the distance it rises. In this case, the slope will be the change in the log of burn rate divided by the change in the log of the pressure. The second and fourth data points more or less go through the line, so we can use them to get the slope, Table F-2.

Data Points for Determining Burn Rate Equation Parameters
Table F-2

Data Point	Log Pressure	Log Burn Rate
2	2.176	-1.201
4	2.699	-1.000

The change in the log of the burning rate is found by subtracting -1.201 from -1.000 to yield 0.201. The change in the log of the pressure is found by subtracting 2.176 from 2.699 to get 0.523. The slope is then 0.201 divided by 0.523 to yield 0.384. So, the value for n in the burn rate equation is 0.384.

With the value of n, we can then determine the value for c. We know the burn rate for the second data point is 0.063 inches/second at a pressure of 150 psi. We can use the following formula to determine c:

Burn Rate Coefficient = c = (Burn Rate)/[(Pressure)^n]

$c = (0.063)/[(150)^{0.384}] = (0.063)/[6.84887] = 0.0092$

Therefore, the propellant burn rate equation for this propellant formulation is:

Burn Rate = 0.0092 * (Chamber Pressure)$^{0.384}$

You can check your work by looking at a few of the other data points. If we take the fourth point which hits the line, we can calculate the burn rate and see if it matches or is close. The pressure for the fourth point was 500 psi which yields a burn rate of 0.10 inches/second using the equation. This matches the data so it looks like we did it right. It's always a good idea to check a few points just to make sure.

Now that you have the burn rate equation, you are ready to design a motor. If you change the propellant formulation, you should redo the strand propellant burn rate tests.

Suppliers of Rocket Parts

Appendix G

You can buy a lot of the parts you will need to make amateur rockets from a variety of companies. I've listed a few to get you started in making your rockets. The listing of these companies is not an endorsement of the company or it's products.

<u>Airframes, nosecones, parachutes, etc.:</u>

LOC/Precision
Box 255
Macedonia, OH 44056
(216) 467-4514

<u>Airframes, nosecones, parachutes, etc.:</u>

Public Missiles Ltd.
349 Cass Ave., Suite C
Mt. Clemmens, MI 48043
(810) 468-1748

<u>Metal tubes, phenolic sheets, rods, o-ring material, rubber sheets:</u>

McMaster Carr Supply
P.O. Box 54960
Los Angeles, CA 90054-0960
www.mcmaster.com
(310) 832-8836

<u>PVC pipe, PVC sheets, PVC brackets, phenolic rods, phenolic sheets:</u>

United States Plastics
1390 Neubrecht Road
Lima, OH 45801
www.usplastic.com
(800) 537-9724

Propellant chemicals, metal powders:

Firefox Enterprises
P.O. Box 5366
Pocatello, ID 83202
208-237-1976
www.firefox-fx.com

Parachutes, Streamers:

Top Flight Recovery
S12621 Donald Road
Spring Green, WI 53588
(608) 588-7204

Purple Woody Reload Motor Hardware & Electronic Deployment Systems:

Missile Works
P.O. Box 740714
Arvada, CO 80006-0714
(303) 426-1462
www.missileworks.com

Data Acquistion Hardware:

Dataq Instruments
150 Springside Drive, Suite B220
Akron, OH 44333
(800) 553-9006
www.dataq.com

More suppliers can be found at our website: www.space-rockets.com/resource.html

Thrust Coefficient

Appendix H

$\gamma = 1.22$

P_e/P_c	ϵ	$\epsilon(P_e/P_c)$	$C_{F_{vac}}$	$C_{F_{opt}}$
.47517	1.0000	.47517	1.23194	.75677
.39486	1.0500	.41461	1.25344	.83884
.34695	1.1000	.38165	1.27191	.89027
.31158	1.1500	.35832	1.28834	.93002
.28351	1.2000	.34021	1.30319	.96298
.26036	1.2500	.32544	1.31677	.99133
.24078	1.3000	.31301	1.32929	1.01628
.22393	1.3500	.30231	1.34090	1.03859
.20924	1.4000	.29293	1.35172	1.05878
.19629	1.4500	.28462	1.36185	1.07723
.18478	1.5000	.27717	1.37137	1.09420
.17447	1.5500	.27043	1.38035	1.10992
.16518	1.6000	.26429	1.38883	1.12454
.15677	1.6500	.25867	1.39688	1.13821
.14911	1.7000	.25349	1.40452	1.15104
.14211	1.7500	.24869	1.41180	1.16311
.13568	1.8000	.24423	1.41874	1.17452
.12976	1.8500	.24006	1.42538	1.18531
.12430	1.9000	.23617	1.43173	1.19556
.11923	1.9500	.23251	1.43781	1.20531
.11453	2.0000	.22906	1.44366	1.21460
.10606	2.1000	.22273	1.45468	1.23195
.098650	2.2000	.21703	1.46490	1.24787
.092118	2.3000	.21187	1.47444	1.26256
.086320	2.4000	.20717	1.48335	1.27619
.081141	2.5000	.20285	1.49172	1.28887
.076491	2.6000	.19888	1.49960	1.30072
.072294	2.7000	.19519	1.50703	1.31184
.068490	2.8000	.19177	1.51407	1.32230
.065027	2.9000	.18858	1.52074	1.33216
.061864	3.0000	.18559	1.52709	1.34149
.056295	3.2000	.18015	1.53889	1.35874
.051558	3.4000	.17530	1.54966	1.37436
.047484	3.6000	.17094	1.55955	1.38861
.043947	3.8000	.16700	1.56869	1.40169
.040852	4.0000	.16341	1.57716	1.41375
.038123	4.2000	.16012	1.58505	1.42494
.035701	4.4000	.15709	1.59243	1.43535
.033539	4.6000	.15428	1.59935	1.44507
.031599	4.8000	.15167	1.60586	1.45419

$\gamma = 1.22$

P_e/P_c	ϵ	$\epsilon(P_e/P_c)$	$C_{F_{vac}}$	$C_{F_{opt}}$
.029849	5.0000	.14924	1.61200	1.46276
.028264	5.2000	.14697	1.61781	1.47084
.026822	5.4000	.14484	1.62332	1.47848
.025505	5.6000	.14283	1.62855	1.48572
.024299	5.8000	.14094	1.63353	1.49259
.023191	6.0000	.13914	1.63828	1.49913
.020778	6.5000	.13506	1.64925	1.51419
.018778	7.0000	.13144	1.65912	1.52768
.017095	7.5000	.12822	1.66808	1.53986
.015663	8.0000	.12531	1.67626	1.55095
.014431	8.5000	.12267	1.68378	1.56111
.013361	9.0000	.12025	1.69072	1.57046
.012425	9.5000	.11804	1.69716	1.57912
.011599	10.0000	.11599	1.70316	1.58717
.010866	10.5000	.11409	1.70877	1.59468
.010212	11.0000	.11233	1.71404	1.60171
.0090941	12.0000	.10913	1.72367	1.61454
.0081773	13.0000	.10630	1.73229	1.62599
.0074130	14.0000	.10378	1.74008	1.63630
.0067674	15.0000	.10151	1.74716	1.64565
.0062156	16.0000	.09945	1.75364	1.65420
.0057392	17.0000	.09757	1.75962	1.66205
.0053242	18.0000	.09584	1.76514	1.66931
.0049599	19.0000	.09424	1.77028	1.67604
.0046379	20.0000	.09276	1.77508	1.68232
.0040949	22.0000	.09009	1.78379	1.69370
.0036559	24.0000	.08774	1.79153	1.70378
.0032945	26.0000	.08566	1.79847	1.71281
.0029923	28.0000	.08379	1.80474	1.72096
.0027364	30.0000	.08209	1.81047	1.72837
.0025171	32.0000	.08055	1.81571	1.73517
.0023274	34.0000	.07913	1.82055	1.74142
.0021619	36.0000	.07783	1.82504	1.74721
.0020163	38.0000	.07662	1.82921	1.75259
.0018874	40.0000	.07550	1.83312	1.75762

ϵ = Exit Cone Expansion Ratio

Drag Coefficients

Appendix I

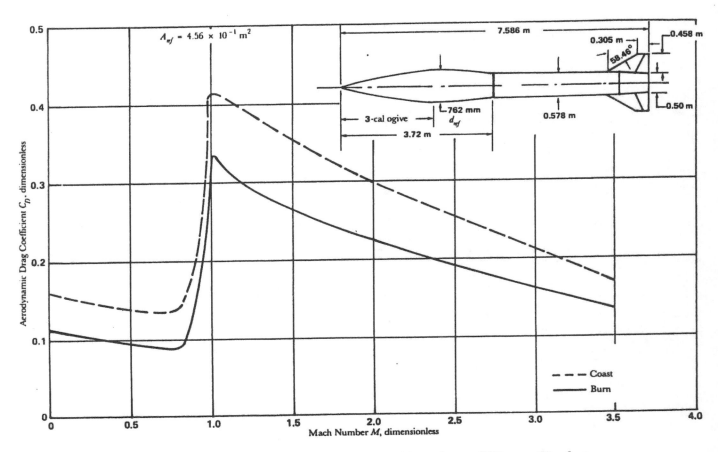

Drag Coefficient vs Mach Number—762-mm Rocket

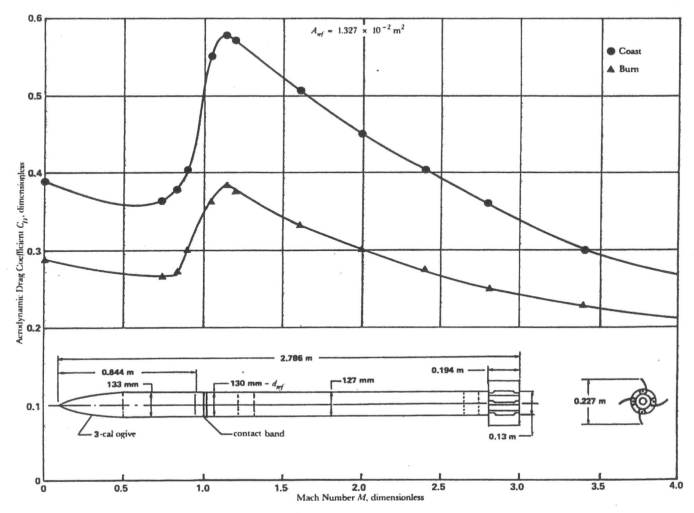

Drag Coefficient vs Mach Number—130-mm Rocket

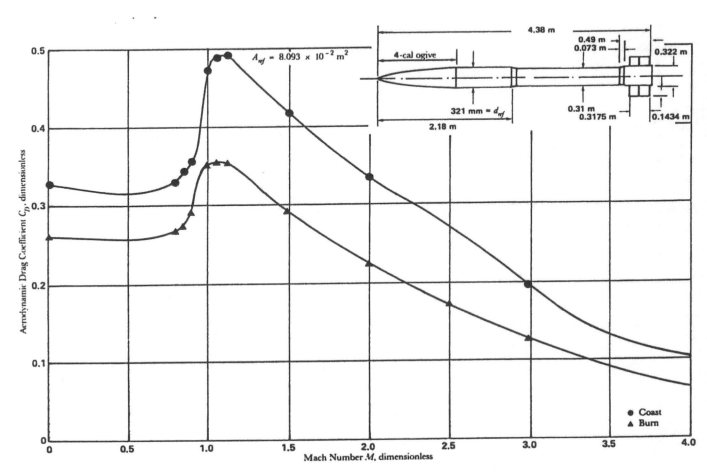

Drag Coefficient vs Mach Number—321-mm Rocket

Some Rocket Designs to Get You Started
Appendix J

We have included four motor designs using PVC pipe and fittings to help get you started. Here are some rocket designs you can use with those motors. You can make these as they are or modify them.

1.75" Diameter Rocket

This rocket uses the 1" PVC pipe motor. It a great starter rocket and will go out of sight on a long smoke trail. The 1" motor will fit perfectly inside our 1.75" diameter body tube. Make the body tube 2 feet long and put three fins on it. The fin dimensions are shown in Figure J-1. Make the fin out of 1/16 inch thick PVC plastic. The fins can be glued on using PVC cement and PVC fin angle bracket.

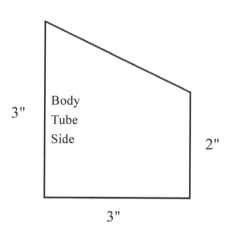

Figure J-1: Fin Dimensions for 1.75" Rocket

3.25 Inch Diameter Rocket

This rocket works well with the 2 inch PVC pipe motor. With some small spacers the 2 inch motor will fit nicely inside the 3.25 inch body tube. The body tube should be in two sections connected by a coupler. You can put an altimeter deployment or timer in the coupler as shown in the book and video. The overall length of the rocket should be approximately 6 feet. Put three fins on it with the dimensions shown in Figure J-2. Make the fins out of 3/32 inch thick PVC sheet unless you will be using a

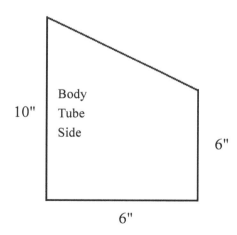

Figure J-2: Fin Dimensions for 3" Rocket

real strong, high thrust motor, then you will want to use 1/8" thick sheet. You can glue the PVC fins on using PVC cement and PVC angle bracket. If you use a strong motor, you should bolt the fins on using aluminum angle brackets.

4.25 Inch Diameter Rocket

This rocket is powered by the 3 inch PVC pipe motor. It fits perfectly inside the body tube. The length of the rocket tube should be about 6 feet. Use a coupler to connect the two body tubes. You can put your electronic altimeter or timer inside the coupler section. The rocket has 3 fins with the dimensions shown in Figure J-3. Use 1/8 inch thick PVC sheet and bolt on the fins using aluminum angle bracket.

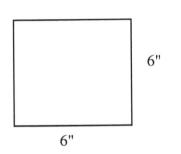

6"

6"

Figure J-3: 4.25" Diameter Rocket Fin Size

6.30 Inch Diameter Rocket

This rocket uses the 4 inch PVC pipe motor. You use little spacers on the motor so that it fits and is centered inside the body tube. The rocket body tube length is 10 ft with a coupler in the middle. You can put your electronic altimeter or timer in the coupler section. It has 3 fins with the dimensions shown in Figure J-4. Use 1/8 inch thick PVC sheet for the fins and bolt them on with aluminum angle bracket.

General Comment

You may want to switch from PVC sheet to grade XX or grade CE phenolic sheet for rockets with large fins or that will be going very fast. It is stronger than PVC sheet.

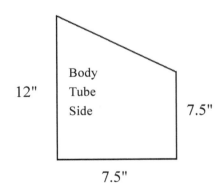

12"

Body Tube Side

7.5"

7.5"

Figure J-4: 6.30" Diameter Rocket Fin Size

Going Into Space and Orbit
Appendix K

In the last couple of years there has been a lot of interest on the part of amateurs in building rockets that can go into Space or into orbit around the earth. Much of this stems from the snail like pace of NASA to get the cost of getting into Space down to reasonable levels. Things are actually going in the wrong direction; it gets more expensive with each passing day. There is certainly no incentive for the major aerospace companies to bring the cost down as they each have their "Cash Cows" like Delta, Atlas, Pegasus, Titan, etc. The launch costs for using these vehicles now controls the design of interplanetary probes, satellites and missions. The designer has to design for the cheapest launch vehicle, which means small and light so the entire project can stay within budget.

I have received many phone calls and e-mails from amateurs that want to go into Space with their rockets after reading the book. Much of this was sparked by the CATS prize, which was terminated in 2000. It provided prize money to anyone that put selected weights up to given altitudes. No one was able to compete for the prize money as the government kept all competitors grounded with endless red tape as people tried to get permission to launch.

With all of that as background, I decided to add this new section to the second edition of the book. I will not focus on the political problems, but rather some of the technical obstacles of getting into Space and orbit. Ironically, getting into Space is really within the reach of some amateurs today. Now, getting into Space is defined as getting up to an altitude of 60 miles above sea level. A few amateur rockets have gotten up to almost 40 miles in altitude. To get into Space, it just a matter of getting enough propellant into a rocket and aiming it straight up. Using the equations and techniques in this book will get you to the point where you can do that.

Getting a payload into orbit is another thing. It is not just a matter of getting up to around 150 miles altitude, but you have to get a tangential velocity of almost 18,000 miles per hour. That takes bigger rocket with a lot more propellant than the amateur can probably put together. I have seen numbers floating around the Internet news groups of the rockets weight only 600 lbs that the poster claims can get into orbit. I wish it were true. To build a rocket that just gets into orbit with no payload, just its own inert weight requires a multistage rocket with approximately, 12,000 kilograms of propellant or about 26,400 lbs.

ELV Propellant Weight

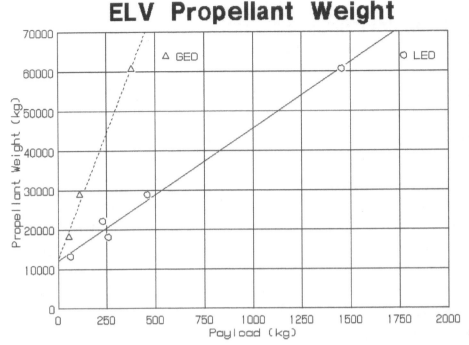

Figure K-1: Typical Propellants Required By Launch Vehicles To Get Into LEO

Those numbers are based on the results shown in Figure K-1, which were obtained by plotting existing launch vehicles with respect to the total propellant weight and payload capacity to Low Earth Orbit (LEO) and Geosynchronous Earth Orbit (GEO). To package this amount of propellant into a three or four stage launch vehicle will take a vehicle on the order of four to six feet in diameter. Assuming you could make such a large multistage vehicle, you would need to fly a precise trajectory in order to get into orbit. This would require guidance and control systems to steer the rocket on a precise path. All of this illustrates the enormous problem of just making a launch vehicle, not to mention alone a low cost one.

Still, you may want to play with the numbers yourself, so here are some equations and general guidelines you can use to outline a rocket that could get into orbit. First, you will need to calculate the velocity increment of your rocket from the propellant. You use the following equation for each stage:

$$\text{Propellant velocity increment (ft/second)} = (\text{Isp}) * (32.2) * \ln(R)$$

$$R = (\text{Initial weight of vehicle}) / (\text{Burnout weight of vehicle})$$

Suppose the ratio of initial weight to burnout weight is five and the specific impulse of the rocket motor is 280 seconds. Then the velocity increment from burning the propellant would be:

K-2

Propellant velocity increment = 280 * 32.2 * ln(5) = 280 * 32.2 * 1.609 = 14,507 ft/second

From the velocity increment, you will need to subtract the energy lost from gravity, which is:

Velocity increment lost to gravity = (32.3) * (Burn time of stage) * cosine(β)

Where:
β = angle between direction of the rocket's travel and vertical.

The actual velocity increment of your rocket for each stage is:

Stage velocity increment = (Propellant velocity increment) - (Drag loss) - (Gravity loss) - (Steering loss)

To get some idea of the loss due to drag, gravity and steering, Table K-1 gives some values for current launch vehicles.

Vehicle	Gravity Loss (fps)	Steering Loss (fps)	Drag Loss (fps)
Ariane 4	5169	125	443
Atlas	4576	548	361
Delta	3772	108	446
Space Shuttle	4008	1174	351
Saturn V	5032	797	131
Titan	4730	213	511

The way to use these equations is to calculate the velocity increment for each stage and then add them all together. From that total, you subtract the gravity, steering and drag loss for the entire vehicle. You can use the values in Table K-1 as a rough approximation for your vehicle. Just pick the vehicle that is closest to yours in shape and trajectory. To get into LEO, you will need a velocity increment of approximately 25,580 ft/second. If you launch in an eastward direction, you pick up about 1150 ft/second from the rotation of the earth at most launch sites. So, you can add that to your velocity increment from the propellant burning.

It is important to note that when you do your calculations, your initial weight for a stage must also include the total weight of all the stages yet to be fired plus the payload weight.

Useful Internet Web Sites
Appendix L

Once you read through this book, you will want to check out some of the following web sites to get more information on different topics.

- Amateur rocketry web site and news forum
  http://www.arocketry.net

- FAA Commercial Space Office - Information on launch licenses
  http://ast.faa.gov

- Material property database
  http://www.matweb.com

- Chemistry database
  http://webbook.nist.gov/chemistry

- Motor and reload designs you can use
  http://www.space-rockets.com/motor.html

- Latest software and software upgrades from CP Technologies
  http://www.space-rockets.com/soft.html

- Amateur Rocketry Society Of America
  http://www.space-rockets.com/arsa

Subsonic Mach Number As A Function Of Area Ratio And Gamma
Appendix M

Mach	$\gamma = 1.0$ Area Ratio	$\gamma = 1.1$ Area Ratio	$\gamma = 1.2$ Area Ratio	$\gamma = 1.3$ Area Ratio	$\gamma = 1.4$ Area Ratio
0	Infinite	Infinite	Infinite	Infinite	Infinite
.05	12.146	11.999	11.857	11.721	11.592
.10	6.096	6.023	5.953	5.885	5.8218
.15	4.089	4.042	3.996	3.952	3.9103
.20	3.094	3.059	3.026	2.994	2.9635
.30	2.115	2.094	2.073	2.054	2.0351
.40	1.643	1.628	1.615	1.602	1.5901
.50	1.375	1.365	1.356	1.348	1.3398
.60	1.210	1.204	1.199	1.193	1.1882
.70	1.107	1.104	1.100	1.0972	1.09437
.80	1.0441	1.0425	1.0410	1.0395	1.03823
.90	1.0104	1.0100	1.0096	1.0092	1.00886
1.0	1.0	1.0	1.0	1.0	1.0